PRISMATIC

I was always afraid of change until I realized that it could only refract my soul into a million different pieces.

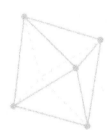

I was always afraid of change until I realized that it could only refract my soul into a million different beautiful colors.

PRISMATIC

VAUGHN-SHANE CAMARDA

PRISMATIC

ISBN-13: 978-0692113424

Printed in the United States of America

To my dad and Trey,
who taught me the most about love and loss.

CONTENTS

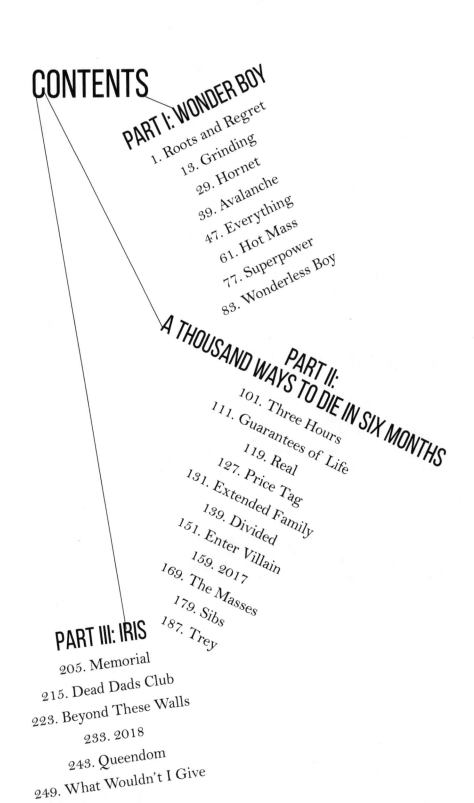

WONDER BOY

Chapter One
ROOTS AND REGRET

"You know, I've tried my hardest to raise you right and show you the way. You're an adult now, and I know I can't be there to always guide you. But trust that God will guide you, and I will always be here if you ever need me," Mom pulled me into her arms and squeezed hard. She sighed into a sob that pushed our chests together and suffocated me with the familiar smell of hairspray and Chanel.

I was the animal caged in holy wire, blessed by good intentions and loved by an incredible mother; a single mom who thought she could help me heal from my identity, but never forced it in my mouth like bitter medicine that tasted of wine and wafer. She tried guiding me into *the right*, but we were both learning about identity together. I didn't blame her. My mom's mission to help me see her version of the truth never stopped her from loving me or from making the sacrifices it took for our survival in a seventies-styled trailer plopped down in rural suburbia. Those sacrifices were endless. Insurmountable, yes. Strong enough to erase our darkest moments together, no.

My mother's first fear for her children seemed pretty standard for most mom's in the world: any harm coming to her kids. Mom's second biggest fear, one of her children being gay, was realized at a time when I didn't know how to erase web browser history. We shared the laptop my dad bought for me, traded it out for my quad when I became even less of an active kid, since the only other person who had a computer was my sister and it never worked properly. It was a sunny day, I was at school, and Mom had used my computer the night before to pay bills. She acted no differently that night or in the morning. What I was naïve to, more than deleting history, was that an attack was cresting the horizon of my heavily closeted world.

Dad picked me up from school early for a dentist appointment because Mom had to work. It had been a while since I saw my dad. My years in high school, when I lived with my mom, left a lot of space between us and our relationship that could be summed up in weekend getaways to my childhood home in the city.

"I'm so glad to get out of school early," I laughed and jumped into his blue Ford truck.

"Yeah?" he didn't greet me with a smile like he usually did, but stern silence that made me hesitate and stare at the Rite Aid we passed by my school.

"Yeah, I totally forgot to do my English homework."

"That's not a good reason to be thankful for getting out of school early. You're better than that, bub," Dad chastised.

"I know, I know. It doesn't happen often," I lied. My grades in high school were barely passable, at best. It was easy to lie to him then because he didn't live with me. Dad was removed from my life because of distance. "I genuinely forgot today."

"As long as you're keeping up on your work. You don't want to end up having to work on bridges all your life like your dad, do you?" he asked.

"No," I focused on the little mechanism that poked out of the door, showing that the door was unlocked.

"You don't like physical work. Never did," he sped along I-79 to Bridgeville where my dentist office sat next to a giant Walmart.

"I'm going to do it once I get home, don't worry," I mumbled and folded my arms over my chest.

Once we arrived, Katy Perry's *I Kissed A Girl* played over the radio speakers in the office. The office reeked like pencil shavings and hand sanitizer. Jerry Springer stood with one leg up on his stage as an odd couple fought on the television and subtitles scrolled one letter at a time along the bottom. It was pretty empty in there, and Dad hadn't spoken a word to me since our brief conversation in the car. *He is probably having one of his days, don't worry about it.*

"Camarada?" they always pronounced our last name wrong, throwing in an extra A between the "r" and the "d."

"Camarda," Dad corrected the assistant.

"Right, sorry," she opened the door for us to enter the white-washed dentist office. Metallic numbers that were supposed to label homes, not rooms, were drilled onto each door we passed. Two rooms down, on the left, we entered into Room 4 and I sat down in the beige dentist chair and breathed in the smell of latex-free gloves and a burning light bulb.

"It looks as if we're going to have to fill in some of these cavities, young man."

"Okay," I sighed, wide-eyed, and thought of every honeybun I'd snuck late at night over the years at my dad's house. He liked to buy sweet things for me. He had just as big a sweet tooth. *Damn your low self-control.* Back lowered as I outstretched against the dentist chair, they wheeled in a silvery tray of an array of giant needles, drill equipment, paste, and multicolored liquids in small white containers.

"Can you numb the outside first? I hate needles," I shook in my seat as he stuck his fingers in my opened mouth and widened it.

"Sure, yep," he turned to scoop some opaque gel and rubbed it on my gums. "Don't look, now," he warned as he dropped something loud on the metal tray holding all of the tools they'd use to drill into my mouth. "Stay very still and make sure you do not open your eyes, okay?" he clarified.

"Uh-huh," I choked on my own spit before the assistant used the vacuum to suck up the liquid in my mouth. Telling a young person not to do something was like giving money to a gambler and telling them not to spend it. I peeked once, only once, and blinding light flashed in my eyes as it reflected off of the giant needle he'd dug into my mouth with over and over again. If I wasn't such a dramatic child, I would've believed that he had his leg up on the chair, elbow propped high, and using a jackhammer to inject my gums with whatever numbing medication they used. My imagination was very extra.

"Alright, I'm going to start drilling now. Let me know if you feel any pain."

The buzzing vibrated across my mouth and into my skull. It didn't hurt, thankfully, but I wasn't really sure how I'd tell him even if it did with his hands half in my mouth and a drill digging into my teeth. The first round of drilling stopped as he repositioned it against my tooth.

"Your mother called me last night and said there were naked photos of men on your laptop," my dad might as well have tackled me out of my chair as the drill started into the tooth again. The dentist hesitated for only a second, the cycling engine cutting out for less than a second before revving up even louder. My eyes opened and stared directly into the light, hoping it would blind me to death if that was even a possibility.

"Why do you think I got your laptop for you? To look up naked photos of guys on the internet? What in the hell, Vaughn? You know this looks bad on me to your mother, right? I'm the one who got you that damned laptop! If you think you're going to just pull one over on me and look up trash on the computer, then you have another thing coming!" Dad got louder as he continued to yell at me while the dentist drilled into my mouth. "I'm not going to be made the bad guy here!"

Heat pulsated in my head, out of sync with my heartbeat. Tears fell and burned my eyes from the bright light shining in them. I tried to look at the dentist and tell him to take the drill gun and just drill me till I'm dead, but I couldn't see his eyes from behind the multihued light. I blinked over and over again, trembled in that dentist chair, while Dad yelled for the entire procedure.

"You're smarter than that!" Dad yelled as the engine struggled to drown him out into background noise.

On the car ride home, Dad finished the paralyzing, traumatic experience he'd started in the dentist office.

"Do you like guys or what? What is wrong with you? Was it something I did, because you know how this looks," Dad's voice was raspy and quieted from the amount of yelling at the dentist's. "Is this a phase?"

What is wrong with you? You're disgusting. Even your own father thinks you're disgusting.

"Yeah, it's a phase. I'm not gay. I don't like guys at all. I just was looking up other stuff and it spammed my computer and appeared. Like pop-ups! I swear. I didn't intentionally look those up. It was just a phase," I fumbled over my words as I held back from crying again. All I thought about was how many conversations I'd come up in at stranger's dinner tables, where they'd talk about the kid who got reamed for looking up naked men on his laptop by his father while he got cavities drilled out of his head. How brutally ironic.

That wasn't the last horrific experience of when my homosexuality got me into deep trouble. It was 2010 and I'd just learned about the magic of Grindr and lying about your age. It was an 18+ app but I was only sixteen years old. To say I was a promiscuous kid would be an exaggeration. Simply put, I was curious. I lived in a home where my mother's beliefs preceded her into our wood paneled rooms, blanketed in dark beige carpet. I wasn't allowed sleepovers with friends who were boys, not even friends who were girls. Any and all sexes didn't matter to her because I was already dangerous to my own salvation and she needed to protect me from my youthful mistakes.

It was too easy back then to lie about your age on those apps. I knew I was talking to people who were over the age of eighteen. The extreme danger being a sixteen-year-old on an adults-only app didn't register in my head. This was my rebellion story and I was my own Katniss Everdeen—pissed off at the powers and acting out for the sake of personal sanity. Then I met a nineteen-year-old college student attending Penn State University. He lived in Squirrel Hill with his parents and we talked for days on end. I was very honest with him about my age. We talked about what he was comfortable with and how this would be the first person I was ever with, and that my mom had some serious control over what I could and could not do. We needed to be crafty, creative, and ballsy.

We went to the movies a lot. I'd tell Mom I was going to the movies with my friend Brittany, since Mom seemed most okay with me hanging with her later at night. It was the first time she loosened the reigns she had wrapped and kept taut around my shoulders. We did this for the entirety of his winter break from college, all the way up until the night before he went back to Penn State main campus in the middle of Pennsylvania. I had musical practice for the spring musical and he picked me up in his parents' Mercedes-Benz and we went to go see Avatar for the fourth time that season because it was the longest movie playing and we wanted to spend the absolute most time together. Once it ended, we both held hands proudly, a sense of electric pride that I was feeling for the first time in my entire life, and walked back to his car to take me home.

"Did you want to go home yet? Are you tired?" he asked.

"A little, but I don't want you to leave yet," I squeezed his hand and kissed it when he started driving back along Old Steubenville Pike. We stopped at a ball field by a church Mom liked to attend and turned off the lights. Pop music played in the background while we leaned against each other and kissed. I wanted him, and he wanted me. Our own little *Romeo and Juliet*, hiding in secret. We didn't care if it killed us. It felt right to us and I was all too aware of what I wanted. We moved to the back of the SUV, seats down so we could cuddle and talk about the possibilities of our future, and I kissed him like we were invincible.

Ryan and I were there for all of fifteen minutes before a bright light beamed into the window and banged on the door.

"Open up!" a man yelled. "Open the door, now!" he got louder.

"Hold on!" I yelled back as I pulled my shirt over my head. The cop's flashlight blinded me as I squinted with my hand over my eyes to shield them from it. This was the end of my life. I was beyond dead when Mom found out.

"What were you two doing in there?" one of the two officers asked.

"We were hanging out."

"Unclothed?" the female officer asked, already knowing the answer.

"Yeah," I mumbled and stared down at the ground.

"How old are you?" the male cop asked next. *Fuck, now you're really dead.*

"I'm seventeen," I lied. *Yep, you're going to jail. Way to lie to the cops.*

"And how old are you?" they asked Ryan.

"Nineteen, sir," Ryan answered as he shifted on his feet and pulled his shirt down more to cover himself.

"Jesus, alright. Get over there," he ordered him away from me as the female officer interrogated him. The male officer interrogated me separately by the Benz. "Did you know he was older than you?"

"Of course, I knew he was older than me. He knew I was underage, too. We're dating."

"Was it consensual? Did he touch you inappropriately without consent?" he asked, triggering anger in the pit of my stomach. I knew where their game was going. This was nothing but consensual. I really liked him, and I pursued more with Ryan. Nothing more, nothing less.

"Absolutely! It was all consensual!" I argued.

"Call your parents," he let me use my cellphone to call them. Dad was the first person I thought to call.

"Hey Dad," I nearly choked when he answered.

"What's up, buddy? I'm away at work."

"I'm kind of here with the police," heat flashed into my head, and I remembered when he punished me in the dentist's chair two years before.

"What?" he went off. *This was a mistake. This was a huge mistake.* "Call your mother immediately! What in the hell, dude? This is not cool! We'll talk once I get home, you hear me? You're stressing me out!"

"Okay, okay, Dad, I'm sorry. Let me call Mom. I have to get off the phone. I love you," I tried cooling him down.

"I love you too, Vaughn-Shane. You need to be smarter about the choices you make. Keep me informed, okay?" he hung up the phone before I could say goodbye.
"He wasn't the smartest choice to call, I don't think," I looked over at the cop and back at my phone to call the last person I wanted to call that night. Mom.

My mom and her weird boyfriend at the time came to pick me up at the ball field and take me to the hospital to get an STD test. After I was done getting tested at Ohio Valley General Hospital, I was taken to the station to be interrogated by two male detectives that had me recount my story not once, but three times in total. Every grueling detail, from both the sexual and non-sexual interactions I had with Ryan, my conversations on Grindr, to any experiences I had outside of those two things at school. I had to go into embarrassing detail with the two detectives, my mother, and her boyfriend in the room.

"So, you're gay?" she asked in front of the detective.

"Yeah, Mom. I'm gay. It's not a phase."

For the first time, in front of a room full of people I never wanted to be with, I admitted who I was for as long as I can remember; I'm talking from the first memory I can possibly remember, around the young age of six.

"When did this happen? Did someone touch you? What happened?" she asked as she wiped away shameful tears in her eyes.

"No, Mom. I just like guys. That's it. No one touched me inappropriately as a kid, no one forced me to do anything now. It was consensual. I wanted to be with him. I'm gay."

Mom and I fought a lot for the second half of my time in high school. It left me with a strong urge to stay at school for as long as humanly possible, with the haunting of our fights in the small confines of the trailer. At school, I could be free and ignore the warzone back at home. I could ignore the moments that haunted me most: when she trapped us in our small white bathroom, screaming at the top of our lungs at each other. I pushed her against a wall once as she held my laptop in her arms because all I wanted to do was write when she thought I was only capable of looking at unclean pictures on the internet.

"What are you doing? You put your hands on your mother!" she screamed at the top of her lungs as she broke down and cried on the bathroom floor. This wasn't who I was, but I wasn't being heard or understood. I was the one backed in the corner, not her. I was the one thinking I was defected, sinful, and lost to the devil because of my roots that were always there. *You are the problem. You will always be the problem, always defected and broken—less of a human and unsalvageable.*

Dad honked the horn as Mom and I squeezed each other in one last embrace before he lugged the last of my furniture to his house. We planned on me moving into Dad's house after high school graduation for college reasons. I needed to use the bus system and there was no bus that went out to where my mom lived.

"I love you, Mom," I kissed her on the cheek as we reconciled our four-year war in four minutes.

"I love you, too, sweetie. Be safe," she rubbed my cheek with her hand and let me go to start my new life in the city. There was a lot of power in love and how we shared it. There was plenty of room for error in our growing understanding for each other, Mom and I, and we managed to come out of the holy warzone changed, but not defeated. Dad honked the horn again for me to hurry as a storm started to roll into town.

Mom raised me in the best way she knew how to—a single mother of three. We fought a lot and maybe her beliefs got into the way sometimes, but I found that the same God we both believed in wasn't the type to damn someone for something that was in the base of their design. Regardless of the arguments and difficult situations I put her through with my poor decision making, she loved me unconditionally. That was what she struggled with most, I believe. While she fought with her religious beliefs and her unconditional love for me, I saw it as suppressive and controlling, and I saw her as scared and unsure of what to do. As much as this move to the city was a new chapter in my life, it was a new chapter in my relationship with my mom. I let go of the arguments, the past disdain for her decisions, and every destructive word I ever said to her as I hopped into the front seat of my dad's truck. We were capable of change and that was all I could hope for us in our future.

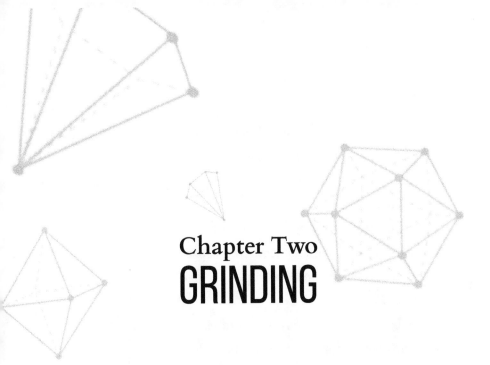

Chapter Two
GRINDING

The first adult job I ever had post high school was in a lawyer's building, smack dab in the middle of downtown Pittsburgh. My role was vital to the success of over three-quarters of the building. The redundant, grey-washed office clerks and lawyers relied on me to get the job done right, fast, and efficiently so they could keep functioning at corporate America speed.

"Kyle, here's your grande Americano!" I slid the cardboard sleeve over the soft white cup that partially hid the green twin-tailed siren logo underneath. Customers that waited for their shot of liquefied adrenaline glared me down like I'd personally insulted them because it wasn't their order being called out. Truth is, Kyle's order was the newest order and I'd skipped the others because he was one beautiful, attractive man. He looked at the others waiting in line as he hesitantly walked up to the handoff counter and nodded to me. *He nodded at me.*

"Thanks, Vaughn," Kyle picked up his steaming cup of coffee, gifted right from the coffee deities, and man-strutted to the exit in his form-fitting business suit.

"No problem," I giddily whispered and watched him leave. *Creepy, I know.*

"Come on, girl, cups don't fill themselves. Pick it up to throw it down!" Brandon, the barista that trained me, snapped his fingers and single-handedly gave me three orders to handoff to anxious customers.

"Sorry, sorry," I cleared my throat and threw an empty caramel macchiato cup underneath the espresso machine, hit a few buttons, and let the vanilla syrup turn black as the milk steamed next to it.

"I saw you write your number underneath his sleeve," Brandon turned to stare at me as his order finished steaming.

"It was just a doodle," I shrugged. "I always draw on the cups."

"It was a doodle in the shape of your phone number and you definitely do not draw random numbers on cups. You draw smiley faces and short-blipped inspirational quotes I swear I saw on Martha Stewart's card collection down at Rite Aid," Brandon snapped his fingers and turned back to pour the hot milk into the espresso-filled cup.

"You're being dramatic," I cackled, which gave away my defense immediately. I've always been the absolute worst liar.

"Real talk, though," he drizzled hazelnut sauce on top of the cup and closed the lid. "Courtney! Hazelnut macchiato at your friendly handoff counter. See you tomorrow, sweetie," Brandon waved at her and walked back over to his espresso machine. "You're gay, yeah?"

"Ye-," the answer caught in my throat. I swallowed the spit I'd almost choked on and coughed hard, "Yeah, why?" My defenses geared up for battle.

"I knew it! Okay, perfect," he started on his next drink as I drizzled caramel topping on the macchiato Joyce had been waiting on for at least eight minutes.

"Caramel macchiato for Joyce!" I yelled. "Sorry for the wait," I flinched as she picked up the cup with an eyebrow raised in blatant annoyance. I wasn't worried, though. She'd be back tomorrow. Joyce was a creature of habit. She wouldn't break up with the coffee shop in her building. "Why perfect?" I started on the next two drinks.

"Because it's my birthday," Brandon clapped his hands together and turned toward me again, "which I forgive you for not telling me 'happy birthday' earlier because you're new and I didn't tell you. But next time, I won't be as forgiving."

"Oh cool, happy birthday," I looked at him as our drinks prepped to finish.

"Thanks! Well, I'm going drinking tonight. I want you to come with me and my friend, Corey. Okay? Cool, I'll see you there," he wiped his hands on his apron and started the next order in line.

"Wait, I'm not twenty-one yet, so I can't go out to bars or even drink. Also, won't it be awkward to have a third wheel around your boyfriend?"

"Excuse me?" Brandon shot a death glare at me. "I'm single as a Pringle and you can't only just have one at a party!" he laughed hard.

"I don't get it," I sprayed syrup into the bottom of an empty cup.

"Well, kind of like, I'm not dating anyone, and you can't just have one Pringle ever, so it makes total sense!"

"So, you have multiple boyfriends? I'm confused," I might have not known the expanse of gay culture at that point in time, but I knew that being a third wheel is the most awkward social position, and I wasn't old enough to drink anyway. They'd laugh at my sad looking driver's license and point me to the closest Mc-Donald's Play Place—with the sad looking ball pit that smells like feet, and those little chairs that look like the Hamburgler, and that purple monster I never knew the name of.

"No, no," he groaned. "Corey is not my boyfriend. She's my best friend, and it's Thursday, hunty! Thursday's at Cruze is college night! Eighteen plus, baby, and we're going to get hammered before we go. That way you can loosen up, because we all know you could use some loosening."

"What's that supposed to mean?" I felt my face flush in a second.

"You're a little stiff and uncomfortable in your own skin. Let's get you liquored up and ready for the candidates who *aren't* married businessmen."

"Kyle's not married. I looked!" I yelled all too loud for how small the coffee shop was.

Fuck.

"See? You need a night out. Please come out?" Brandon nearly begged as he hoisted up a gallon of milk from the fridge below the espresso machines.

"Fine," I gave in. "I have to go home and shower, though. I refuse to go out looking like this and smelling like dirty water and old coffee. They'll think I'm homeless or something."

"Wait till you get to my age, when you don't care what you look like going out," Brandon clicked his tongue and slid another empty cup my way.

"You're not even old," I dramatically rolled my eyes and caught the cup mid-slide.

"Old enough," Brandon booty-bumped me.

"Doubtful," I smiled big. I didn't really know if this made

us friends or not right away, but it sure as hell felt like it. *My first gay friend that didn't want to hook up with me.* Pure magic. I loved every single moment of that feeling. Even with coffee, syrup, and steamed milk stained across my apron and arms, I was glowing, and feeling the gayest I had ever felt in my entire life.

"Also, real talk," he shoved his hands into his apron pockets and leaned close so only I would hear, "Kyle's hot and all, but who we really need to be going after is our boss."

"What?" I cackled loudly in protest. I would never hit on our boss, nor did I find him attractive. Side note: both of those were lies. All. Lies.

"Don't act like you haven't given him that thirsty look you've been giving every man in a suit that's walked in those two glass doors. He's hot and you know it!"

"Okay, it's not every single business guy that walks through the doors. Greg walks in those doors every single day with his business suit and I don't even bat an eyelash." Greg was a regular, and he was old enough to be my grandpa.

"Oh, please. Girl. Our boss is hot, and you know it. Do you like guys or don't you?" We laughed hard and started wiping up the counters when the rush died a little. "So, be at my place around five or six tonight?"

"I'll be there. Just text me your address," I rung out the coffee-stained rag into the metal sink and shoved it back underneath the espresso machines.

Brandon lived in the South Side slopes—a very dingy, but hipster-dingy, neighborhood. The bus dropped me off at the end of a steep hill that reminded me of the hill Dad and I lived on in Beechview, but this was much less steep than ours. I dialed his number and it went right to voicemail.

"Are you shitting me?" I was halfway up the hill when the

maps app on my phone said I had reached his home. I was out of breath and dry-mouthed. I was the skinniest I've ever been and in my prime for those crucial, exploratory gay years, when it was all about image and how funny you were, but walking up that damned hill had me wildly out of breath and low-key sweaty.

"Hey bitch!" Brandon yelled from a brick porch at the curve of the hill.

"You didn't answer your phone!" I yelled back in heavy breaths.

"I didn't have my phone on me, calm down. It's not like I abandoned you out in the middle of the slopes or something," he disappeared into his tall red patchwork house and appeared seconds later, two stories down from a basement door.

"Welcome to my wonderful abode. We have a wide range of colors all around and outside the house that I'm sure you'll just love to look at. You stare at it in awestruck beauty and wonder to yourself, *Why?*" Brandon turned on his Midwestern housewife accent he loved to toy around with at the coffee shop. It made me laugh hard, and I'd even try talking in the accent, too, but I wasn't as good as him.

"Really, though. Why are all the colors, metal, and different kinds of siding meshed all together?" I asked.

"Don't ask me. We just rent the place," Brandon lit another cigarette and puffed it lightly while we sat on the crumbling cement city steps along the side of his house.

"You and Corey?" I positioned myself away from the cigarette clouds he breathed out.

"No, Corey lives on the North Shore. You know Jen and Kristen from work, yeah?" he tapped the ash off his smoldering menthol Camel Crush and leaned against the wall of his house.

"Yeah, why?"

"I live with them. Jen has her demon dog here. Fair warning, he's an asshole to everyone, so don't take offense. Kristen's boyfriend is over here, too. He's not an asshole like Jen's dog, but he kind of looks like a dirty Jesus and has lost some of his marbles."

"Oh?" I giggled as he put out is half-smoked cigarette.

"You know, for being a baby gay, you sure know how to dress for the club. Are you sure you've never been to the club before?" Brandon shoved his half-smoked cigarette into the missing slot in his pack before sliding it back in his pocket.

"Promise. This is all very new. Drinking, too," I shied away, a little embarrassed.

"Aw, honey," he tapped my shoulder lightly, "let's get you learnt and turnt. Come on." Brandon grabbed my hand and we walked the rest of the city steps up to the porch he'd been standing on before. Red brick encompassed the sitting area, and an old couch that I swore some type of animal had to be living in sat in the middle of the porch. Kristen's boyfriend sat on the couch with a low burning blunt in his hand and smiled at me. His teeth were brown and spotted, but his disposition was friendly enough.

"Hi," I waved at him. "I'm Vaughn. I work with-,"

"James," he cut me off and nodded. James held out his blunt and offered a hit.

"Nope. I don't smoke. Even cigarettes," I folded my lips tight and shook my head in a kind decline.

"Suit yourself," he raised his blunt at me in cheers and took a huge puff. The smell of weed reminded me of long car rides on vacation when a skunk sprayed near the highway, or of home, when my Dad would hang outside for hours on end in the summertime and smoke. It was twofold for my Dad. He liked smoking recreationally, but it also helped equalize him. Having borderline personality disorder, balance was a difficult thing to find.

"Come on, let's get you drunk," Brandon held open the screen door for me and I followed down the metal-plated stairwell to a multicolored kitchen.

"Why are there so many colors in this house?" I sat on the metal step as an incredibly angry, mostly hairless, and ugly dog came bolting out of a bedroom door right at me. *This is it. This is how I die.*

"Jack!" Brandon screamed its name and scooped the dog up in his arms. "Be nice to our guests! Demon dog," he gently tossed Jack onto Jen's bed and shut her door before the dog could escape. "Told you."

"I'd be angry, too, if I was as ugly as Jack," I laughed and felt my phone vibrating.

"Jeeze, Mr. Popular. Who's hitting you up?" Brandon brought out a box of brownies, oil, eggs, and a bottle of whipped vodka.

"Grindr. I'm fresh meat in this part of town."

"No abandoning me for a hookup. It's my birthday and you already made plans with me first!" he smacked my calf, uncovered by my ripped jean shorts, with the clean spatula.

"Oh, my goodness, there will not be any hooking up with anyone tonight. I can promise you that."

"Mhmm," he gave me a side eye when he tossed me the box of brownie mix. "We're making drunk brownies! Then drinking and eating them before we leave. Cool? Read me the directions," Brandon snapped his fingers and spun the glass bowl. My mom had the same one back in Imperial.

"You do know the heat will cook out the vodka, yeah?" I raised my eyebrow at him.

"I don't want to hear any of that science shit. Just read me the directions please," Brandon waved the spatula at me and started cracking the eggs in the bowl.

"Do you really need me to read the directions to you?" I asked.

"No, but it saves you from the dogs on Grindr, so do it anyways," he mixed the ingredients together as I read the directions in my best Midwestern housewife voice. "See, you're getting the hang of it!"

"It's addicting," I cackled loudly as feet clamored down the kitchen steps.

"Hey boys!" Jen yelled as she carried store-bought sushi in one hand and a bottle of red wine in the other. "What're we baking tonight?"

"Vodka brownies!" Brandon yelled back.

"Vegan?" her intrigue piqued.

"No, sorry," Brandon threw the brownie batter into the oven and set the timer for forty minutes.

"Damn you," she grumbled and put her red wine on the spice rack across from the table, shoved in a tight little corner. "Fine, you get none of my sushi."

"That's fine, sushi doesn't do anything for drunkenness anyways. I'm getting Vaughn wasted for my birthday."

"I don't know about wasted, but," I uneasily laughed with thoughts of how much I hate throwing up to begin with, let alone not being in control of my body.

"Oh, shut up, you're getting drunk and we're going to Cruze," Brandon whipped around to point at Jen opening her bedroom door. "By the way, wanna come to Cruze tonight for my birthday?" he asked her.

"Nah, Justin and I are doing date night tonight. Sock will be on the door, please don't come drunkenly knocking on my door after the club tonight," Jen glared at him as she pet Jack on her bed.

"Gross. But fine," Brandon pulled out a bottle of whiskey and two shot glasses. "Want a shot for this lovely Thursday evening?" he looked back at Jen on her bed.

"Sure, why not," Jen scurried out of her bedroom and shut the door so Jack wouldn't escape. Of course, Jack started whining and barking once she had, but she didn't pay him any mind.

"To my majestic birth out of my mother's vagina!" Brandon raised his shot of dark brown whiskey. Jen raised her shot glass and waited for me to join them.

"That's a weird thing to cheers to, but here's to it!" I uneasily smiled and clanked my glass against theirs.

"And to new friends, and dancing, and flirting with men, and finding Vaughn a boyfriend, and Vaughn's soon-to-be relationship with our bathroom toilet!" Brandon downed the whiskey like a champ, Jen followed, and I stared at the brown liquor in my glass, feeling an uneasy disposition to all those things as well as this unfamiliar substance in my hand. I drank wine till I threw up once before. It was chardonnay and even that burned my throat, now turning my stomach at the sight, sound, and smell of it. I couldn't imagine what this would feel like coming back up.

Here's to not getting drunk tonight, Vaughn.

I threw the whiskey back and felt it all the way down into my empty belly. The burn was unexpected and caught in my throat, so I choked for about five minutes trying to clear it, waving my hand repeatedly to let Brandon and Jen know I was okay, even though my eyes were watering uncontrollably from the sting.

"Woo!" Jen clapped her hands and pulled out a pizza menu.

"Yes, pizza please," I choked out the words, feeling the churning liquor inside my stomach croak with hunger pains.

We walked down the South Side slopes to South Side proper and made our way through the crowds of college students screaming, cheering, and stumbling along the road. These college students looked different than the ones I saw at community college. They were messy but beautiful, careless and vibrant. These students were from the bigger colleges in the city, no doubt, and it made me wonder what other types of humans I hadn't seen yet as a so-called "baby gay," as Brandon had dubbed me.

Greasy pizza and whiskey coursed through my veins as I felt my body vibrating with the passing bass of cars, taxis, and mini-vans, full of college students trying to get their shot of life with a vodka chaser. Brandon stopped me as we made it to one of the bridges that crossed into the city, handed me a headphone, and we danced the rest of the way to the club, listening to RuPaul's newest album that I felt all too deep in my bones.

"Are you ready for this?" Brandon pulled the headphone out of my ear as we walked up to the entrance of the club. It was bathed in rainbow dance lights and I could hear remixed Whitney Houston songs blasting. "I got him covered," Brandon handed the doorman ten dollars for the cover charge, grabbed my hand, and led me away from the bald-headed bouncer, uncomfortably eyeing me up with incredibly hungry eyes.

"Hey!" A girl waved excitedly from the dance floor with another girl next to her.

"This is my new friend, Vaughn. He's new at the coffee shop," Brandon screamed in her ear, yelling over the blasting dance music.

"I'm Corey! This is my girlfriend, Natasha," she pointed

over to the white girl shyly standing next to her, like Corey was her bodyguard.

"Nice to meet you!" I yelled.

"What?" Corey leaned in closer to my mouth.

"Nice to meet you!" I tried yelling louder, but it's always been hard for my voice to carry. Corey excitedly shook her head and took her girlfriend away from the black-wooded dance stage and toward the bar.

"Want anything to drink?" Brandon asked me.

"I can't drink, remember?" I yelled.

"I have you covered," he left me alone on the dance floor as a flood of people ran in when Whitney Houston transformed into Robyn's "Dancing on My Own."

"This is my jam!" Brandon ran back with warp speed and a can of PBR and pulled me into the middle of the dance floor. "Drink up! Come on, big gulp!" he shoved the can in my face and I downed what felt like half of it.

"Okay," I coughed at the bitter beer taste. "Not my favorite, but I appreciate the offer."

"You'll get used to cheap beer at bars. It's the best way to have a good time on a budget."

Corey came back with Natasha, fresh tequila dripping from their lips, and started dancing with Brandon. I was incredibly buzzed, yes, but not enough to lose my inhibition. While Brandon tried bringing me to life, grabbed my hand and jumped around and danced freely, I stood there, paralyzed by the hundreds of eyes on me—whether they were actually on me or not. I stood out more by just standing there than I would've if I'd just danced with them, but I couldn't help it. Old men on black leather couches watched as the youthful danced freely, untouched, maybe only for a moment, by the ugliness that was outside those light-stained walls, filled with theatrical smoke and deep beats.

"Come on, dance!" Brandon yelled at me.

"What?" I heard him but asked to stall time.

"Dance!" he shook my arms like spaghetti noodles, put his hands on my shoulders and shook me up and down to move.

"I don't really dance," I confessed and folded into my unsure self.

"I don't care! Just start moving!" he yelled and let go of me.

Slowly, uneasily, I started to bounce up and down to the music. Every voice drowned out underneath the hard beat of the music that echoed inside my head.

He dances weird.

Look how bald he is. Where did your hair go?

Why don't you have abs? Do you even go to the gym?

You're wearing a five-dollar shirt from H&M.

You don't belong here.

You don't belong here. You should leave.

Leave. Leave now.

This is what an anxiety attack looks like. Surprised?

I froze, looked around with beads of sweat dripping from the humidity inside the club. Limbs hit me from all around as drunken youth danced around me, letting their cares fly with the wind, but I was barred from the freedom they took for granted. I was not one of them, and they could smell me from a mile away. I knew it. I looked all around, anxious for an escape but nothing was there to help me. No beacon, no white flag, or even a red escape sign. I would've taken even the restroom sign at that point. I was drowning in a sea of people who all had their opinions of me but didn't even know me or look at me. One big flash blinded me as Brandon took my photo.

"Oh, my goodness, what are you doing?" I laughed at Brandon and hid my face behind my hand.

"Please dance?" he asked and put his phone away.

I paused for a moment, hearing the music die down and the lights lower to the floor as the sea of people stopped jumping for a second. My heartbeat slowed, and the pulse of the music synched with the eighties drumbeat before the music exploded and the DJ lights blinded me. I jumped up and around with my hands in the air, feeling the rhythm and only a sliver of freedom that I thought I knew all about. The light didn't bounce off my image but pierced through me as the bass heightened my senses. I smiled big, cheering underneath the loud music as Brandon, Corey, Natasha, and I danced until we sweat and nearly collapsed.

I'm not sure if this was what sublime freedom was supposed to feel like, if this was permanent or temporary, but I knew that my anxiety didn't live there. Expectations of how I should look, where I should be, who I should look at, and how I should dance didn't exist. I wanted this moment to last forever. I was dancing on my own, without the company of my crippling anxiety to tear me down and keep me there. This was how unfiltered pride and belonging felt. I tasted the sweetness of the nectar and felt every color for the very first time through my body. Pride was never an idea or action, it was a feeling deeply rooted inside me, just waiting until the first euphoric release into every color of the spectrum. Whether it was the alcohol, lights, music, or Brandon that finally pushed me over the edge, I could be myself there with them.

Chapter Three
HORNET

"Tell me everything!" Brandon pulled me aside before we walked across the Smithfield Street Bridge, over to the Mononga-hela Incline. "Where did you meet? Have you done the dirty yet? Is he good in bed? Girl, I want details!"

"Oh, my goodness," I waved him away as I choked on my iced green tea latte while we walked across the bridge together. The golden hour sunlight looked best on Pittsburgh. It made the city look like a movie set and we, the extras, were sprinkled along the city streets.

"Okay, well, maybe not everything. But at least tell me how you met! Did you guys meet on Grindr?" he heavily sighed with some major side-eye.

"No, no, it wasn't Grindr," I confessed. "It was a different dating app."

"Bitch!"

We laughed loudly as a gang of bikers peddled by us at warp speed and yelled, "Left!"

"It's kind of complicated now, though."

"How? You both just started seeing each other like, what, a month ago? What could possibly be more complicated?" Brandon hiked up his backpack and played some music from his phone that was nestled in the mesh side pocket of his bag. Unsurprisingly, we both matched with jean shorts, tanks, and backward hats. We'd both been screwed genetically with ungracious hairlines.

"He's going to college," I shrugged and smacked a layer of Chapstick on my lips to fill awkward space.

"A college boy! You know how to pick them," Brandon laughed and took a drink of his iced macchiato he'd made before leaving work.

"No, not really. He's all the way out in Titusville. Two hours away driving, and there isn't any bus system or rail that goes that way. I don't even have a car! How am I supposed to do that?" I pulled out my cellphone and texted him a little hello because I missed him. But he was in class still and the receipt didn't change to 'read.' Truthfully, it wasn't my choice to turn read receipts on. I didn't even have them on for my own parents or family, but I supposed it seemed like a minor thing to be okay with when he asked. "I can try to use my Dad's truck, maybe."

"You'll figure it out," Brandon gazed out over the scintillate sunbeams flickering against the dirty Monongahela River water.

"Have you ever been on the incline?" I shoved my phone into my shorts pocket and hiked my backpack up closer to my shoulders.

"Nope! I've been meaning to, but never can do it when I think about it," he looked up at the incline and lit a menthol cigarette he crushed at the filter. Most of my friends tried to keep the smoke out of my face because they knew I didn't smoke, but the wind always had a different plan.

"Let's go do it!" I walked ahead of him to the beat of his music pulsing from his cell phone and he quickly caught up, dancing along the bridge. At the end of the blue and gold bridge we strutted along, we crossed West Carson Street and continued to dance to the little red building with steep tracks jetting out of the back of the building.

The incline was my favorite as a kid. Really, anything with tracks intrigued me and I'd obsess over them. Inside the Freight Shoppes in Station Square, my parents would take me and my siblings to the toy store, where it had one of those wooden train layouts in the back and they'd let me play for hours and hours, circling around the wooden tracks until they probably wanted to scream from boredom. But I could have stayed there forever. The toy store had since closed down as the Freight Shoppes declined and bars and restaurants took over.

"Hey," a message from John ignited my phone screen in my palm as Brandon and I waited for the funicular at the bottom of the track. Warm oil wafted into the building from creases and cracks in the light yellow and orange sliding doors that blocked off the actual track and the passengers. Dark orange tile, that I knew I saw once at McDonald's or Wendy's before, was slick with pop spilled from a cup at the top of the platform.

"Hey you, how was class?" I replied.

"It was alright. Stupid. We aren't learning anything that I don't know already," he replied in seconds.

"Oh nice, haha. Sorry about that," I bit my lip as the doors opened and spewed out families, joggers, and tourists who rode the mountain car down.

"No worries. What are you up to?" John rapid fired question marks, impatiently awaiting my response.

"On the incline with Brandon! It's great," I fired back and

slid down in the wooden seat, so we could watch ourselves rise up from the city we stomped through so frequently.

"Must be nice. Have a good time," John's bitterness shot like a spear through the phone and into my chest. He let the water inside and tanked my mood because nothing was worse than disappointing the one I was so deeply infatuated with.

"What's wrong?" I replied desperate and panicked. "Hello?"

He read my messages but didn't reply right away.

"I just don't understand why you think that'd be okay to do that with your friend who's gay," John aimed his gun at my chest and blinded me with his words. This anger was something I never experienced, and I hated the heavy feeling it gave me, like I had been unfaithful to him.

"He's a good friend of mine, we've never been sexual with each other, and it was a last-minute thing. I'm sorry," my palms perspired, and my balding head flashed with heat.

"It doesn't matter. You go to gay clubs with him and think that's okay to do when you know you're taken. All those faggots probably grinding up on you, buying you drinks, and you not caring how I feel," John pulled the trigger and decimated the space inside my chest. This was a war I was going to lose by nature because the only flag I ever had in my artillery was the white flag of submission.

"I'm not like that. I barely even dance in the clubs at all. I just stand there because I don't want to put myself in one of those positions. I wouldn't do that. I wouldn't allow that. I know I'm taken and I act that way. I don't know where this is coming from. You said it was okay to go that night, why didn't you tell me otherwise if you had a problem? I'm confused," I felt my eyes bounce around the keyboard on my phone as I typed a million miles per second, thumbs tapping loudly on the glass screen protector.

"Damn, slow down there. Everything alright?" Brandon asked, but he was background noise, muffled by the loud clicking of the metal wheels crossing small gaps in the track, and the buzzing anxious panic that pulsated inside my ears.

"Hello?"

"I'm fine, sorry. Nothing to worry about," I shoved my phone in my pocket before John replied.

"Are you sure?" Brandon asked.

"Positive," I put on my best fake smile and looked over at him, so he'd believe me.

"Alright, well, let's get off this thing and get some food, yeah?" he asked.

"I don't—," my phone vibrated repeatedly as John rapid fired texts soaked in gasoline and set ablaze.

"You can't keep living like you're single anymore. What the fuck, dude? You don't treat the guys you're with like this—going out with your gay 'friends' and doing shit you do with someone you're dating," John handed me the rope, already tied in a noose.

"I'll just stop talking to him," I put the noose around my neck and looked up at the rope that disappeared into the dark oblivion above my head.

"How are you going to do that?" John guided me to the edge of the floor, where dark water flowed freely beneath the edge of this cement cliff.

"I'll just cut him out. Won't explain anything or whatever. I'll fix this," I felt the cold cement underneath my feet as John held my hand and caressed up my arm to my ear.

"Okay," he sent. "I have class. I'll call you later."

"Okay," I walked off the cliff and felt the rope tighten

around my neck.

"Vaughn?" Brandon placed his hand on my shoulder as we stood at the viewing platform, feet away from the funicular terminal. "What's wrong?"

"Nothing, I'm just not feeling well and I'm tired. Can we postpone dinner to another night this week or…?" I wore a thin smile and shoved my phone in my pocket.

"Yeah, of course! We can plan it whenever. I'm heading back home to visit family, but when I get back, we can go out," Brandon put in his headphones and scrolled through some music on his phone. "I'll see you next week," he waved and left me alone on the viewing platform as the sun set sharply on Pittsburgh's skyline.

Brandon hadn't known that this was goodbye for a long time, maybe even forever. I didn't tell him I was transferring coffee shops while he was away visiting family to make John happy. It was an easy transfer, and John seemed satisfied at the severed friendship I'd cut out of my body and left on that cement viewing platform to shrivel up and die off in the weather. It didn't stop with Brandon. It rattled through everyone I held close to me, carved me hollow, because I strived hard to live a life selflessly pleasing John, so I would never feel his accusatory finger push hard against my forehead. I'd kill for him and he knew it. So, when it came down to a happy life with my first actual love, he turned the gun on me and kissed me while he told me to pull the trigger. The Wonder Boy gifted his power in a glass box to the boy draped in golden-crusted ruin.

"Come on!" I laughed loudly from my dad's truck window as John jogged lazily toward me from his dorm door.

"Want to meet my friends?" he tossed his backpack through

the window and onto the passenger side of the truck.

"Can we after we check into the hotel?" I pursed my lips and turned down our song that I'd played loudly for him to hear.

"Yeah, sure!" John hopped into the truck and we drove off to one of the only hotels in Titusville, Pennsylvania. A small group of trains connected together with little porches and lights on the outsides of the doors, The Caboose Motel had to have been the most unique place I've been in.

"I hated going so long without seeing you," I kissed him at a red light before it flashed green.

"I missed you too, beebs," he called me our stupid little pet name. "Does your dad know that you have the truck?" he asked.

"No, so let's keep it that way."

"You badass," he laughed and tickled my side.

"Stop that!" I cackled loudly and hiked my bag up over my shoulder in front of our room for the night. It was freezing inside our assigned caboose. There was a small piece of laminated paper sitting on the bed with instructions on how to work the small number of amenities in our room. There was a television at the end of the bed, a bathroom, and a dual heating-cooling unit just by the drafty door. "Did you listen to that song I sent you yet?"

"Of course, I did, I loved it," John kissed me on the cheek and stole my phone to scroll through music, or messages. I couldn't react any certain way, though, or else he would accuse me of being suspicious and throw me out to sleep with the wolves.

"This was it, yeah?" he chose the Coldplay song and let it play loudly from my phone as he motioned for me to follow him into the shower. Our love wasn't perfect, but maybe love never is. I knew what I felt was crazy love for John. There were no corners in my mind that would think to be unfaithful to him, so I never worried, thinking there was no plausible way for him to be unfaithful to me. That doesn't happen when two people are in love because there is no room for it. The reassurance helped ease my mind and let me fearlessly be with him in mind, body, and soul. I loved him more than I loved myself.

"I have a surprise planned for Christmas," I confessed as the hot water hit against our bodies in the tiny plastic shower, the floor bowing beneath our weight.

"Really? Already? What's that? Tell me!" John tickled my sides and it nearly made me slip and fall in the shower.

"Fine, stop tickling me though so I can talk," I crossed my arms to hide my stomach. "I planned a trip for us to take a train to Chicago. I already bought the tickets!" I smiled in expectation of the same reaction. I was wrong. "I'm going to pay for the whole thing," I continued, "and I have some other surprises picked out, too. It'll be fun! Why don't you seem excited?"

"No, that's great that you're going to pay for everything, but I would have to ask my parents first. You haven't really seen much of them enough yet. I don't know if they'll allow it," John turned away from me and rubbed shampoo into his hair.

"You're eighteen. Why would you have to ask for permission?" I leaned against the back of the shower and hiked my arms up higher across my chest.

"What do you mean why would I have to ask my parents? They're my parents. Of course, I need to ask for permission," John shot a look with one eye and shampoo covering the other.

John's family was his everything. They were what I called a "fairytale family." John's father was in the navy, and their family moved around a lot, which ripped away all of John's friends repeatedly. The only constant in John's life was his family, making them closer than usual. John was one of four siblings, and his parents were still together. They went to pumpkin patches together, ate family dinners together, supported each other, had Christmas together, and family game nights. I've seen these fairytale families throughout my life, but I've never had to date someone who had one. While I had to fend for myself in my independence as a young adult, John had this intricate web, created over years of memories, where everything needed to pass through before becoming acceptable or real.

"Fine, but I already bought the train tickets and booked the hotel room," I reached for the towel, dried off, and wrapped it around my body to lay on the floral-patterned king bed spread.

"I don't know why you're getting mad at me. You are the one who bought the tickets without even asking," John walked out of the bathroom, dripping water onto the ground from his fingertips.

"I'm angry because you're an adult and that defeats the purpose of a surprise," I shut off the music and turned the dial up on the HVAC by the bedside table.

"You told me what the surprise was, so really, what's the point?"

"That's because you literally asked—never mind. Forget it. I'll cancel the trip," I pulled up the Amtrak site on my laptop, tapping loudly against the keys, and watched water droplets fall onto the smooth plastic covering of my computer.

"Don't cancel it. You're being dramatic. Damn. Let me ask, that's all I said. You're blowing things out of proportion. Chill out, dude. Otherwise, you can just take my ass back to the dorms and you can leave."

"I'm sorry. I just didn't expect that reaction and I was disappointed. Just ask and hopefully they'll let you, I guess," I shut my laptop and plopped down on the bed. "Can you lay down with me?" I didn't want to be close to him, but physicality spoke more apologetically than words did to him.

"Sure," he crawled next to me and rested his head on my chest. Hesitantly, I wrapped my arm around his soft shoulders. Familiar hellfire guilt crawled from underneath the bed and lit the duvet on fire that we slept so peacefully on. He made me want to burn up in this caboose room because I'd done something wrong again, when all I wanted was to do the right thing. He stripped me down to nothing and threw me out into the cold rain that pounded the roof of this shambled home, held together by surface level love and sex because it felt good. I accepted this normality of ours. However fucked up it was, in servitude, I became accustomed to his insecurities and let the fire engulf me into a suffocated sleep with him nuzzled perfectly on my chest, safe and soundless.

Chapter Four
AVALANCHE

I sat in a row of gray plastic chairs inside Amtrak's Pittsburgh Station. It wasn't the first time I'd been to Chicago; I lied to my dad once so I could go visit a longtime friend of mine in Wisconsin, but I flew instead of taking the train. Dad thought it was a trip for my community college's politics club to watch President Obama speak at the University of Wisconsin's Madison campus. I saw President Obama speak on campus, but it wasn't with my politics club (sorry, Dad).

There was no better feeling then when I sat anxiously in the station, waiting to board. I was escaping the city and my singular overwhelm. This was a lonely journey, but all freeing, like I had been caged much longer beyond graduating.

"Now boarding," the electronic voice echoed inside the station when the forest green, sliding glass doors opened and allowed our small group of strangers toward the track. I expected to see what I saw in movies—white smoke that bellowed from the bottom of the cars as farewell kisses and hugs were exchanged between loved ones. It was *very, very* different. The only smoke that bellowed out came from two or three passengers grouped closely to the open doorway, smoking their cigarettes. Three conductors stood a couple cars apart to scan tickets before new passengers boarded. As we funneled down the dimly lit cement platform, the first conductor scanned my ticket and led me to the second to last train car.

"Watch your step," the conductor held her arm out into the entryway of the car. Intense bright silver carried from the bodies of the cars into the interior walls of the less-than-grand foyer. Gray floors with scintillate specks spotted the walkway to the lower-level seating compartments. I chose the most available seating, which was up the spiraling staircase, on the second floor of coach class. Seated in rows of two, sleep sunken passengers barely startled when we filtered into our assigned seats. Somehow, the train gods were kind this time and let me have a window seat so I could rest my head against it, using my University of Wisconsin hoodie for a pillow.

The dim blue light ignited the middle walkway of the train where others settled or walked around to stretch their cramped legs. As we crossed the unlit metal bridge over the Allegheny River, banked around the edge of the North Shore, and sped behind PNC Park and Heinz Field, I watched as my sleeping city blurred through the streak of cold December rain. The twinkling lights faded away into sunken shadows that hung heavy over extinguished mills and warehouses along the Ohio River. Sleep swooped me off my feet as I felt stickiness between my eyelids strengthen; the farther I was away from my haunting in Pittsburgh, the better that I could push it down into the black water that collected in the prison inside my chest.

My trip to Chicago was before I could legally drink. One of my good friends bought Angry Orchard for me to take on the train because they don't check baggage or carry-on luggage. It was the same trip that I realized, and would never forget, that their bottlecaps are not twist-off. On the marble floor of my hotel room bathroom that night, I sat trying to get bottles of hard cider open with everything from a lighter to a belt buckle—basically anything that I could read quickly on the internet. By the way, the belt works. Just don't smash your fingers or elbow off any sinks while trying to unhinge those babies. Also, bottles don't fit in the mini fridges. Nor do mini fridges keep anything cold for very long. Did that stop me? No.
Should it have? Probably.

This was the first time I'd had dinner ninety-five floors up from street level. I rode the elevator to the top of the John Hancock building, to the Signature Room, and sat along the window, where fiery orange lights ignited the nightlife below, screened by a snowy haze. No doubt, I was the youngest one having dinner at this wildly expensive restaurant, but it was worth every penny. A few inches of glass separated me from the incredible space between my small body and the city below. While I stuffed my face with buttered bread and squid ink linguine with scallops coated in a sublime butter-garlic sauce, I stared out at the infinity I wanted to drown myself in; an invisible electricity I wanted to reach out and touch and feel through my skin, muscles, and down to the center of my bones. It was like falling in love all over again—a love that would not break me, or keep me in a cage, or push me over the edge to plummet a thousand feet below. In that moment, I felt the first crack of lightning in a wintry sky, but nobody else could see it. It was a rush of feeling all at once, like I was king of my world, and as some otherworldly oracle, I saw my unbreakable future.

This is where I belonged—where my soul was born in a cosmic crack of energy in the middle of a lightning storm. Someday, somehow, I would escape back to this city. I'd lived here in a past life, long forgotten.

For some reason, it felt super appropriate to book a Segway tour in the middle of winter in Chicago. I wanted to be that amount of extra back then, so that was a thing. Also, I think I bombarded the tour guide with a million and one questions about the Divergent movie which, unfortunately for him, he never had watched.

"I think I remember the filming for that, though. They shut down the entire section of Upper Wacker by the Hyatt Regency and the Swissotel to film it. Traffic was a nightmare. It's always like that, though," he spun around quickly to end the conversation and continued on with the tour.

"This is beautiful," I sighed as my group crossed the bridge, underneath the holiday decorations, toward the Magnificent Mile. It was a clear night and the city wasn't as windy as usual. Our last stop on the tour was a holiday-themed market that looked similar to the one in Pittsburgh's Market Square. Similar red tents strung with clear bulbs lit the maze of popup shops and home-style eateries, wafting bratwurst and other German delicacies into the air. "One... two hot chocolates, please," I nodded to the woman running the bratwurst tent.

"Twelve hot chocolates?" she asked.

"Uhhh," I looked over at the empty row of Segways lined up along the wall. "No, two," I confirmed.

"Six dollars," she handed off two paper cups filled to the brim with sweet hot chocolate for me to devour.

"Thanks," he grabbed my arm lightly and rubbed up to my shoulder.

"No problem," I shot a look over to who touched me as snowflakes stung against my eyes and intensified the glowing light of the strung lights between each red and white shack.

John took one of the hot chocolates out of my hand and led me back to the line of Segways.

He had been there all along—with me every minute of this trip. From the ride to Pittsburgh's station, in the hour wait to board the train, along the nine-hour trek across states in a sleep-cloaked link of trains, and the morning we arrived at Chicago's Union Station. He was there helping me break open the bottles without breaking our teeth or skin. John was there when we were on our way to dinner at the Signature Room, and when a homeless person swindled twenty bucks off him. He was there the entire time I gushed about my favorite movie to the tour guide and didn't judge me once for it, unlike the other tourists with me, who, clearly hadn't seen the movie either.

I wrote him out of it because I was happy.

This was our first vacation of many toxic getaways, and I already felt alone. There was something about the power behind his intent, words, and actions that isolated me from the bravery I'd built upwards from ground zero. He tore me down to fill the empty spaces inside of him. John tore me down, broke me enough that he could control me.

I didn't blame him, though. I showed him where and how and gave him the controls to my life and my body. He set up walls to isolate me from the people that I cared about while we played happy couple to his friends. Don't get me wrong. I loved him. I loved him so hard that I didn't care if he spray painted the windows that let golden light into my glass house black. The power was his because it was all I could give that would please him.

I have zero pictures of my time with John. After the end of his era, the years together made me an empty shell and wore me like a pair of clothes, easily thrown away. I deleted everything. I erased a war history that was made for stories I thought I'd never write (jokes on me, yeah?). I created the perfect monster. Someone so easily hated for their wrongs and someone who never could do right. Funny thing was that I loved every piece of him so much, it drained every ounce of my energy. I avoided my family, cut out friends, and accepted things that the new-Vaughn I built, post high school graduation, would have never allowed. If I hadn't believed he was the one for the rest of my life, that love was flawed and that it was okay to allow someone to control every inch of your life because of their own insecurities and desires, then I would have been out much sooner and with a lot less damage.

I had to figure the hard shit out for myself. I had to suffer. I had to scream in silence underneath his pressure, to burn bridges between incredible people I became so close with. I had to beg, run myself into debt and emotional ruin, and give up dreams I voiced to him alone for his approval—that he shot down so easily with judgment and disapproval. I had to accept everything that he made me think I was, even if I wasn't. I took the staple gun and closed my mouth, taped over my eyes, and gave him the reigns to every part of me because I was dying to please him and comfort him. I gave so much of myself to someone whose toxicity ran deep inside their own soul.

I made my own mistakes, too. I cheated after months of snooping through his phone and seeing texts of things we didn't even say to each other and photos exchanged between random guys with every part of his body. Tumblr, Snapchat, Facebook, texts, you name it. All I did was return the favor, and he, unfortunately, found out. It wasn't my proudest moment, but I thought that was normalcy. It felt wrong. I was miserable and cannot forget the day when that ugliness violently surfaced.

Our time wasn't always bad, though. And it would be unfair to speak of it like he was this wicked human from sweet beginning to stark end. John's family was beautiful and took care of me and accepted me in so many ways I never thought possible. They treated me like one of their own kids and supported me in the small endeavors John and I put our energy into—whether it was tie-dyeing Lucky Brand underwear for Easter, or any of the small trips we took down to Orange Beach, Alabama, and the countless times we traveled to Chicago. We experienced a lot of life, John and me. He was my first love, which is why I think I allowed so much of myself to be erased by him. When we didn't fight or he didn't exercise his strength against me, we were a force to be reckoned with. That's what tripped me up every time we tried to end things. We both remembered the good and slipped back into old habits.

I spend a lot of time thinking about what I might have done differently. The walls I repaired in my glass house have never really been quite the same—something skewed and warped in the shape of the glass that molded into the old pieces, untouched by the war. I resented writing this entire second chapter of John, even though it helped me realize a few important things about myself:

I survived the pounding, destructive weight of an avalanche suffocating my soul.

I would never let anyone or anything have that power over me ever again.

I spent years focusing on how John warped and shattered me after we expired.

Even though he destroyed a lot of shiny parts of me, there is something powerfully beautiful about the brokenness that grows through from ash. I held onto him way after he had left. Blamed him for problems I pushed down into a drawer, which I promised myself I'd empty when the time was right. I never emptied it like I said I would and carried him with me for all this time. So, here we are, four years after John and I ended, finally doing what I wanted to do years ago.

This is the end of our line.

Chapter Five
EVERYTHING

We met on Grindr.

Listen, I hear you. No story that begins with *"We met on Grindr"* is a strong start, but it was our truth.

This meet-up was incredibly sporadic, and I don't think

we spoke much before that day, nor did he even have a photo of himself for his profile, which I thought was weird. I'd just had a float session at Levity in Squirrel Hill and we were meeting at one of my favorite bars on Mt. Washington. The Summit makes the absolute best Old Fashioned in Pittsburgh. It was small, dark, and hipster enough to be cozy and personal, but with enough exits to disappear if he wanted to kidnap me.

Evening sunbeams painted deep oranges across the buildings and a softened blue sky extended into the star-dotted sky. He walked into the bar as I cursed at the lack of parking spots near the entrance. My escape plan was not exactly as I'd mapped out, so I shared my location with Brandon in case things got fuzzy.

"Be safe, bitch!" he texted me before I shoved my phone into my pocket and walked into the bar.

The bouncer immediately made me pull out my ID to check my age before letting me on through to go meet up with my date. At the bar, the murphy bulbs glowed fiery orange against his perfectly slicked back blonde hair. His glasses hid his blue eyes with the reflection of the outside light. He licked his lips before he flashed blinding pearly whites. My escape plan was thrown down the closest flight of stairs, and I felt my cheeks flush red. Thankfully, my plan to meet in the darkest and most public place worked in my favor and hid my warm, red cheeks. Unless the dark light was making them worse, I thought, then I was fucked. There went my anxiety again.

"Vaughn?" he asked while he sat to the side and faced the empty bar chair next to him.

"James?" I asked and took my seat. "Nice to finally 'meet' you!" I pulled out one of my classic Grindr jokes because meeting someone on Grindr wasn't really meeting—it was deciphering if they wanted a hook up, picture of the goods, or if they were actually a decent human being (not in order of actual importance or occurrence).

"You as well," he giggled at my joke, which made me smile hard. His laugh was golden. Any laugh that made me smile or laugh back was perfect in my book. "You must do this with all your meet-ups, huh? What number am I this week?"

Woah there, bud. You are number twelve but don't start pointing fingers. Total joke, by the way. He was number one.

"No, definitely not another for this week. I don't usually do this at all. It's pretty new," I swore his eyes sparkled when I said that. Unfortunately, that was a familiar reaction in Grindr culture. Everyone expected a slut-oppotomas, but there are some genuine people on Grindr who aren't as confident socially as they might be behind the screen of a phone. Plus, the whole *Is-He-Gay-or-Does-He-Just-Have-Nice-Taste-In-Style* game was exhausting for us gays since Pittsburgh boarded the metrosexual train.

"Well, that's refreshing to hear. Me too," he sipped his Moscow Mule and nodded to the drink menu.

"Old Fashioned, please," I smiled at the bartender as he clicked and clanked metal to glass to muddle the orange and cherries. The aroma gave me chills. The temperature was absolutely perfect inside the bar as the bartender worked magic while I tried not to slobber in front of this wildly cute date.

"Old Fashioned, huh?" he asked.

"Yep, just like my soul. It's my one-and-done, though. Any more after the one, I'm a little too buzzed to keep my dignity," I laughed and flashed him a side-eye look that meant total business. This felt normal and natural. We talked for hours on end until it was too late to be out for a Monday night. My one-and-done turned into three-and-overdone. James unexpectedly paid for the entire order and he sweetly invited me to stay at his apartment, so

I didn't have to drive. "Where did you park?" I focused really hard on not slurring my words or walking weird.

"I walked," he shrugged as we walked down Shiloh Street to Virginia.

"Walked? Do you work... live close? Sorry," I dropped my head in embarrassment because I slurred my words. I wasn't drunk; only warm all over and a little loose from the bourbon.

"Yep, right down the hill! What kind of person would I be if I let you drive? Neither of us should be driving, so walking is the only option," James grabbed my hand and led me down the hill toward the intersection. "Just make a left here," he guided me left as we laughed and chatted lightly about things we love and what we'd like to do in the future. He was a nurse practitioner in Ohio—something I wouldn't remember about him come morning. It didn't matter, honestly. I grew up without money, and I felt that was obvious to him by my reaction to him picking up the tab.

"I appreciate you," I squeezed his hand lightly, "for picking up the bill and not making me drive home."

"Don't mention it," he led me down his road to a peach-colored duplex and up a mountain of cement steps.

"All these steps are a deal breaker," I pulled away from him.

"Are they now?" he laughed and guided me with a steady hand in the small of my back up the stairs.

"Absolutely," I giggled and willfully followed up the stairs to his door.

His home smelled like waffle crisp, like soap and vacation and city. "Your apartment's beautiful." Carpeted stairs met bright wooden planks that ran vertically across his entire apartment to the laminate, grey and bronze-colored tiles in his kitchen.

"Thanks! There's a deck out back but it's not cleaned so you can't look at it," he tried stopping me from peeking out the back-door window, but my curiosity was no match for his warning.

"Oh, stop. You act like that bothers me. You should see my room," I mumbled and looked down at the leaf coverage on his deck. "There's just some leaves that need swept. Nothing I couldn't handle," I already invited myself into his apartment for a second time past this night. If he even wanted me after this night. "But we should really get to bed," I leaned into him. His breath hit my neck and sent chills down my body.

"I agree. We have work in the morning," James led me to his room and pulled back the covers. They were brown with bright orange and muted yellow strokes dyed into the fabric.

"You have work in the morning. This guy is off the next two days!" I laughed.

"Nice! Well, then I'll see you the next two days," he pulled me into him after we pulled the covers up to our chins.

"If I'm invited, yeah," I teased.

"Oh brother, of course you're invited. I don't hook up and run," his buzz let him slip.

"So, this is a hook up, huh?" I laughed loudly.

"No," he laughed at his slip, "it's not that. I was just seeing what you'd say."

"Oh, I'm so sure," I rolled closer to him and kissed him like I had never been destroyed before; like John never existed, because in this blissful moment, a cosmically-corrected shift in the universe, he never existed, and I was happy to write him down into the darkness. I sprinted so hard from that darkness, from the cracks spewing muddy water.

We got into relational things quickly, within the next couple months—a bag of my clothes stashed in a corner of his oddly angular bedroom and my toothbrush in his medicine cabinet. James said his duplex used to be a fellowship house—a church gathering place of some sort—and his last roommate thought it was haunted. Let me tell you. I woke up every morning at 4am, feeling like I was being stared at, making my stomach churn. To cope, I binge watched Netflix in the living room until James woke up. I knew he felt bad because it was so disruptive to my sleep.

"He'll get used to you," James sighed as he leaned in the doorway between his dining room and living room, where I sat on his couch, curled up in a ball, underneath thick blankets.

"I hope so," I smiled brightly at him. "I wanted to have coffee made for you before you woke up, but I couldn't tell how long you'd sleep for."

"You're perfect," he came over and kissed me, cupping my face with his hands.

"Let me go make you some," I kissed him back and slid along his wooden floors to the kitchen. "Are you hungry? Do you want me to cook breakfast?" I popped the K-Cup into the Keurig and pulled down on his industrial-sized coffee maker.

"You know we don't eat in the morning," he laughed and followed me into the kitchen.

"I know, but I was going to ask anyways," I sipped my cold coffee before tossing it into the microwave for a minute to heat up.

"Just make another cup, babe," he leaned against the kitchen to let me rest my head on his shoulder. It was great that we were almost the same height. He was a little taller, but short enough to make the perfect headrest.

"I know, but I'm not done with this one," I booty-bumped him. We did all the gross things couples do behind the scenes: flirted incessantly, cuddled on the couch for movie nights, helped each other get ready, showered together—almost everything.

"Do you want to know what I got you for your birthday yet?" he shook his arms and made a vibrating noise with his vocal chords that he told me was a habit when he got really excited or home from work. It was beyond endearing.

"You didn't have to get me anything," I rolled my eyes at him. He knew gifts made me super uncomfortable because I wasn't used to getting them.

"I know, but I wanted to, and it's your birthday. There's some thinking involved in this, though. Decision making."

"You're always scheming," I giggled and handed his coffee to him.

"Let me be to my scheming and let me do something nice for my boyfriend, okay?" James led me to the bedroom and we sat down on the messy blankets. I usually made the bed in the morning. He liked when I did that, and I loved making him happy. "So, you have to choose what you want to do and where we should explore."

"Explore?" my ears twitched as my face lit up. On the bed, he set down two yellowish baggies with Illinois and Louisiana stitched in black. One red heart was stitched inside each state: one on Chicago and the other on New Orleans.

"I got us both a trip for your birthday. You need to choose what we do, though."

"What the fuck," I grabbed both bags and squeezed them in complete disbelief this was actually happening. "Are you serious? This is crazy! And I'm super indecisive, you know that."

"Make one decision, please. It's important. I won't make you decide now, but there is one that I hope you pick rather than the other," he looked down as I watched his eyes skim over the New Orleans bag.

"Obviously, New Orleans," I spat out without a second

thought.

Pause.

Okay, so, this is how it happened in my head. James has a different story of how I decided where we went. He can laugh about this later, if/when he reads this.

"Good, because those flight tickets aren't refundable," he took away the Illinois bag and stuffed it into his clothes closet.

"You already bought the tickets?" I gasped.

"It's two weeks away, this was bought weeks ago. I'm surprised you didn't know. Remember that receipt that popped up on my phone that you asked about, when I had to lie and say it was for my parents?" James started changing his clothes.

"You are ridiculous, I had no idea! Holy shit, this is wild," I jumped up and threw my arms around him. My hand slid up his back to his neck and I pulled him in closer to me. James had another habit of playing with my ears, which only made me smile harder when he started folding my left ear.

James showed me the world. New Orleans was phenomenal, even after he slept on the floor with me when I drank way too much and fully realized, for the second time, that tequila pushes me into full-out anaphylaxis. He slept on the bathroom floor with me through it, with a pillow placed underneath my head so I was comfortable, and a big hotel bed comforter over him to keep him warm on the tile floor. He definitely cursed me in the morning when I jumped up perfectly fine and ready for our planned ten-mile bike tour while he nursed an incredible hangover.

I threw caution to the wind as I fell wildly in love with this beautiful person who cared so much for me, showing me places I never even dreamed of seeing. He didn't care about what happened before, neither did I, because we were in this right now. I felt like I could take on the world. It was the world, though, that reminded me of the barren nothingness from before that James met me in. I played a real heavy game, but when my anxiety started piquing and my Facebook memories showed me happy times with John that I knew deep down were topical, it tricked me, and I fell, weighted, from grace.

I slipped first in Toronto. I was way too drunk, and when I went to the bathroom, I had a panic attack James never knew about. I remember everything becoming so dark and gone and I was head deep, submerged in memories that, and I didn't know why there were flashing around me. *Why now? In a Toronto club, wasted out of my mind, around all of these pretty people.* For what reason did John have to creep into my thoughts, where I hid the darkness, in this incredibly beautiful light? He got the invitation to the invisible part and cornered me in the bathroom. And I lost myself, as I finished washing my hands for an unnaturally long time, everything went black, and I woke up the next day with a throbbing headache next to a wide-awake James, staring.

"Oh, my head hurts," I kissed him, but he didn't even flinch. "What's the plan for today?" I assumed he had an incredible hangover, too. I was wrong.

"Do you remember anything from last night?" The question sunk from my ears into the pit of my stomach, like hot lava burning through foliage and bursting into flames.

"What do you mean? Not really, no, why?" I steadied myself as the room started tilting a little toward the window.

"You were dancing around a group of gays and straight-up touched another guys butt. When I say touch, you grabbed, and grabbed hard, and kept dancing. Then, you saw me and walked right up to me and said, *"Hi,"* like everything was normal and that you hadn't just touched another guy. What was that about, Vaughn? Honestly?" He teared up as I sunk into the rapidly spinning room. It wasn't from the alcohol last night. The darkness that cornered me in the bathroom and caught me sent me spiraling down into the nothingness I'd been hiding from. John was never there, but the more drunk I got, the more he haunted me. I remembered crying in the bathroom for maybe a second at best. I remembered shutting off the faucet, angrier than I'd ever been since being with John, and I stumbled out of the bathroom, caught in a constant loop of one of the many times John cheated on me.

"Are you joking? Is this real?" I leaned into the dresser against the wall of the Toronto condo to steady myself. "I am so incredibly sorry. I literally do not remember anything. Holy shit, babe. I'm so sorry," I slid down the dresser and held my head in between my hands as he sat up on the edge of the mattress, watching me spiral downwards.

"No, it happened. What—you're telling me you don't remember that at all?" James crossed his arms.

"No, I don't remember that at all. I never would have decided to do that, I'm so sorry. You have to believe me, honestly," I talked in circles until I felt whatever was in my stomach would come up.

"I—believe you, Vaughn. It just really hurt me," he moped as I looked up with tears welled in my eyes, deep enough to blur him out. "I didn't know what to think."

"I'm so sorry. I would never do that to you," I wiped my tears and stood far too quickly. I pulled him into me even though the room spun wildly while a panic attack grounded me. "I'm so incredibly sorry. I need to go to the bathroom," I let go to wipe my eyes and left him alone in the spare bedroom.

Inside the bathroom, I shut and locked the door so I could fall to the ground alone, against the toilet. Wet tree bark-colored vomit spotted with red projected from my mouth into the toilet as I felt my panic rise and anxiety take over. Throwing up pushed things off for the rest of the trip until it all cooled down between us. James was graciously forgiving, and we stumbled back to our routine in his apartment quickly.

I was going to marry him by the end of the year—near our one-year anniversary. I told you we moved fast, yeah? James and I were moving warp speed into a life of static and trips and big plans. I fucked up and ruined those plans, though. My darkness that I'd painted over started peeking through peeled paint and seeping into the beautiful life that we had together. While we talked about where we'd move together next, I battled against the darkness that quickly ate away at me.

"Remember this?" John messaged me a Facebook memory on some app that I'd forgotten to block him, sending me spiraling backwards. He had no right to come walking into my new life, but he let himself in and I never told him to leave.

"Yeah, good times," I rolled my eyes when I sent the message.

"How've you been?" he asked.

"Really good. You?"

"Good. How's James?" he asked.

"He's amazing, really. He treats me phenomenally. How do you know about him?" I asked.

"Social media lol," he replied quickly. John and I were on the same cellphone plan together—a relic of our past—and I had to meet him every month to get money for it, sometimes behind James' back because I was ashamed to tell him about it. Fear of reprimand came signature with John's controlling habits, and that carried into my relationship with James, even though James never showed himself to be anything like John.

"Cool. Can we split the phones yet?" I asked.

"Sure," he wrote, and we planned to meet later that week.

It was after the Sprint trip that I fucked up and let him back in for one singular moment that destroyed everything.

I cheated. I allowed it. I might not have wanted it, and John might have persuaded me as a "last chance dance" type thing. *One last soiree.* I never stopped it, though, because I never fully dealt with the aftermath that John created before jumping in head first with James.

James didn't know I'd cheated until long after I left him. He thought I needed time and wanted to move back with my dad because things were going too fast. The truth? My guilt ate away at everything I was. I was being water tortured with battery acid. It burned everything inside and I ached for days on end. It damaged me so much that the little things James did would agitate me, and not because it was James, but because I hated everything about the person I saw in the mirror. Everything we'd built, I ran out with, stuffed in black trash bags, as our relationship burned to the ground in James' watery eyes.

"Goodbye," I whispered to him, with my keys in my hand, and the side of my mouth bleeding onto my tongue as I chewed on it.

"I'll see you," his chin quivered as I left. I won't ever forget that moment—I broke him and, mournfully, let my head hang down with shame he never knew I carried.

I loved James with every part of my heart, regardless if it was shattered to pieces. But John created a deep crater inside my soul, and I couldn't allow myself to marry the man I loved with this incredible secret that ate away at me over and over again.

We met shortly after I moved back in with my dad. I drove to my new hotel management job through miserable I-376 traffic to Robinson. He still worked at the hospital in Ohio—out on I-376 in morning traffic, our cars met up next to each other in perfect alignment. What in the actual Hell, Universe?

"Hi," I texted him.

"Still wearing my glasses, I see," he replied back.

"Yeah, I'm sorry. I should return them to you," I yanked them off my face and threw them onto the passenger seat.

"Don't worry about it. I got a new pair," he looked over as I looked away from him to respond and turn the music down.

"Can you play this song?" I sent him *Still Falling for You* by Ellie Goulding. "I was going to propose to you to this song."

"Why are you telling me this? It's too early to start sobbing in my car, okay? Lol."
I knew he was right, but it was the first thing I thought of when I looked over and saw him driving, watching Netflix on his phone, settled on the dashboard, while he drove to work—behavior I always yelled at him for.

"Because I wanted to tell you this was never my plan, and that I was sorry for ruining a great thing. I still care about you and love you, but I don't really have a right to say any of it. Anyways, I'm sorry," I sent as I exited the highway toward work.

"What's in the past is in the past. Let it rest," he sent back. "Have a good day at work."

"You too," I parked my car and rested on my steering wheel to sob wildly before getting to work, where I'd laugh like nothing was wrong.

J.

I texted you after I wrote this chapter because your new boyfriend appeared on the "Friends You May Know" section of my Facebook. It was a cosmic kick in the balls, and I was still so emotionally unprotected from writing all of this about you. I hope, for yourself, that you can truly forgive me, because by including you in my story, this isn't me asking for further forgiveness. I don't need that or you anymore. This is me learning to forgive myself for being human and making horrible mistakes to someone I once loved.

Goodbye,
V.

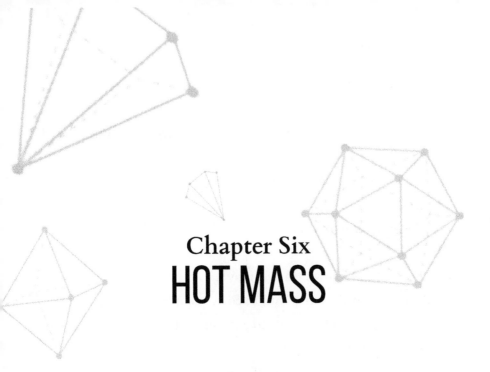

Chapter Six
HOT MASS

There's this meme somewhere out in the glorious internet where there's a fairly handsome guy standing with a bright smile—you know, that kind of run-of-the-mill attractive person you'd see in corporate culture marketing videos or something. He's standing in the middle of a doorway, and above the meme itself, it says (excuse the meme grammar)—

"Dating after a long relationship be like..."

Then the caption underneath the handsome corporate man in the meme says something like—

"So... what's your favorite cheese?"

I breathe, eat, and sleep memes. I don't think I've related to any other meme I've ever seen more than this one because it is exactly how dating is after a long relationship. I will say, though, I didn't jump right into things with anyone. My flirt game was strong before John, and after, I felt like one of those old crooners in smoky dive bars trying to be "hip" and flirt with the younger crowd. I was stripped down and had to start from the beginning. Back into time (back into time).

"Hey bitch," Brandon shot me a text message as I sat in bed, doing absolutely nothing. With all of the unexpected craziness that happens at a hotel day-in and day-out, I was beyond exhausted from my job.

"Haiiiii," I shot back and leaned further into my bed, against my pillow.

"What are you up to, kitten? Anything on the agenda for tonight?"

Now, I'm known through my friend group to have no plans at all, but I'll make some wild excuse, like my cat robbed a bank and I have to go bail her out, to get out of hanging because I am the laziest human.

"Don't start thinking of some excuse. The read receipts are on, I saw you read my message," Brandon replied before I could think of anything useful to get out of going into public.

"Hey, buddy boy," Dad had his work boots on, which meant he was either about to go away for the week or do a small project in the yard or town.

"Hey Dad, what's up?" I kicked the covers away and shut off my television.

"Just about to head out to do some work soon. Doing anything tonight?" he walked over, and we hugged awkwardly from the side. "I'm sorry things didn't work out with James. But I'm happy to have you back home." Dad didn't actually say all of that. He was a man of few words, but I knew him more than I think he realized, and I could see how sorry he was about me and James not working out in the way he sulked. Dad had watched me through two breakups already. John's was ugly and I cried for a very long time. My dad cried with me in our kitchen while we stood at the black-topped breakfast bar he built after he bought the house when I was three months old. This time was different. I played off a graciously adult persona that reeked of guilt he couldn't spot. I was his little boy. Doing wrong wasn't something I was capable of—*often.*

Living back at home centered me. It gently brought me floating back to reality rather than plummeting down to Earth in a fiery ball of rock and gas. My dad loved to cook for me and be around me so it wasn't just him and his girlfriend, Char, who really only mooched off of his money. He wasn't rich by any means, but what we did have, our little existence in Pittsburgh, Pennsylvania, was home.

"Are you leaving right now?" I asked.

"Uhh," Dad hesitated because he knew what I was going to ask next. "Not yet, why?"

"Do you have enough time to buzz my head real quick?" I uneasily smiled in a chuckle as I kicked the blankets totally off and threw on a shirt.

"Aw bud, I don't have *that* much time. Can we do it tomorrow in the morning? Before I leave for the week for work?" he leaned against the doorway to my room.

"Yeah! That's fine. I figured I'd just ask, it's no big deal." Dad was cursed with incredible guilt and fear of disappointing people he loved. It was another little unfortunate add-on that came with his borderline personality disorder. Being aware of his disorder, though, made it super important for me to reassure him. I knew what it felt like to fear disappointing people that I cared about most. It was like this thick, heavy cloud that brooded over you at all times; like being followed everywhere you go by the same looming stranger. Anything I could do to save him from himself, I would do without a second thought.

"Alright, thanks buddy," Dad smiled and tapped the doorframe before clomping down the stairs in his worn steel-toed construction boots. "See you tomorrow!" He started singing *Plush* by Stone Temple Pilots, a song he'd frequently play on one of his guitars at home or just sing out loud because he liked it and didn't care if he wasn't the best singer. I didn't care either. It was the sound of home.

"I'm waiting!" Brandon messaged me again.

"Alright, where are we going?" I replied and rolled out of bed as my cat, Tris, scampered away from her sun patch on my grey bed sheets.

"Have you ever been to the after-hours night at Club Pittsburgh?" he asked.

What did I just agree to?

"Isn't that the gay bathhouse downtown?" I cringed at even the thought of having to only wear a towel in a club, since they have a strict dress code. "Don't they only allow you to wear a towel in there?"

"Yes, but no. One Saturday a month, they block off the second floor and have the after-hours party and serve drinks and all that. It's fun! We're going to go."

"Okay, but I'm not going if I have to be in only a towel." I started the shower to get ready as Tris rolled in to do her daily, awkward stare-down while I showered myself. Cats are weird. Awesome, but weird.

"No, no. They let you wear regular clothes this day. It's like the only day they don't make you wear only a towel," Brandon sent the dancing-girl emoji.

"Isn't called Black Mass or something?"

"Oh honey," he laughed. "Black Mass is a movie. It's Hot Mass. There's not much of a difference cult-wise, but people aren't murdered here."

"My game is so off," I mumbled as we pulled into the gravel lot next to Club Pittsburgh. There were two entrances to this building: one was the actual entrance to Club where clothes were not allowed, the other was the Liberty Bail Bonds entrance where Hot Mass attendees entered.

"Don't worry, alright? Jeeze, you're going to dry up the crowd if you keep worrying so much," Brandon led me to the glass door underneath the green and white Liberty Bail Bonds sign where a singular bouncer stood in front of the door. "Is Hot Mass going on?" he asked.

"Yeah. Password?"

Password? The fuck am I really getting myself into?

"Big black coffee," Brandon waved his hand around like he was brushing away a fly.

"That was last month's password. What's the new password?" the bouncer put Brandon right in his place.

"Dammit, I looked on the Facebook page and didn't see anything about a new password," Brandon crossed his arms and looked around at the line forming behind us.

"Guess we can't go. No worries," I smiled at the bouncer and started to head back to my car, but Brandon was quick and snatched my arm up.

"Don't worry about it," the bouncer looked around to see if anyone was watching or listening to him. "Just go on in," he looked at me with a smile that screamed I looked like a snack to him. *Ugh.*

The stairs were wooden and creaky, painted blue, and darkened as the bright fluorescent light from the bail bonds sign diminished the farther we walked up them. Wood floors spanned the room as red and blue lights set everything in a dark and mysterious hue that pulsated with the deep base vibrating inside my chest.

"Fifteen," the cash register attendant stared at me behind his glasses where the red and blue lights reflected off of them.

"I got you," Brandon moved in front of me and pulled out a twenty and a ten to hand to the guy. "Let's drink," he led me around the corner to a neon sign that pointed downwards to a small opening. There, a skinny white boy stood behind a shady looking opening. On the counter was taped a piece of laminated paper that said "Drinks."

"Two vodka Sprites, please," Brandon tipped the guy pouring drinks, and as he saw the money drop into the tip jar, he brimmed our cups with alcohol and only a baby splash of Sprite. *This is going to be a rough night. I already feel it.*

"Okay, whatever happens tonight, you need to promise me one thing," I yelled over the beating music.

"Yeah?"

"I don't get wasted, because I have work at 6am tomorrow morning, and I don't go home with anyone."

"You're no fun. But fine," Brandon led me around the second floor of Club Pittsburgh to the smoker's room, where only one dude sat with a cigarette slowly burning in between his fingers next to a couple of girls. We dashed out of the softly lit room with a ton of mismatched couches and snaked our way past the scary bar area and onto the dance floor. "We're pretty early, which is why there's no one really here yet."

"That's fine with me," I mumbled and sipped my incredibly strong drink. "Is there anywhere we can sit?"

"Um, other than the smoker's room? No," he looked around at the lack of chairs.

"What's over here?" There was another barely lit room with three to four little boxes with crawlspace entrances in them.

The wooden walls were high enough so you couldn't see into them from the top, and the entrances low enough that no one could see inside.

"Oh, those are usually the sex boxes," Brandon nonchalantly brushed off the question.

"The *what?*" I stepped away from them.

"Well, they're not sex boxes tonight. They're just little cubbies."

"Can we sit in them?" I asked as I got down and crawled into one of the dark boxes. Inside, the music was muffled, and I couldn't see any of the surfaces, which made me wildly nervous and anxious all at the same time, but it was away from people and that felt better than aimlessly wandering around, waiting for someone to approach us. "This is wild," I laughed as Brandon struggled to enter into the box.

"You know, I used to be so much more gracious back in my day. Now these old bones are just struggling to move at all," he started to talk in his Midwestern housewife accent again that cracked me up.

"Oh, just a shame, what are you going to do?" I mimicked his accent as we both cackled together in the weird box. "I'm already done with drink one. Want another?"

"Jeeze, you alcoholic," I handed him my empty cup. "Absolutely."

He crawled back out of the dark box and left me inside by myself. Although probably not in the cleanest of spaces (for the record, it did smell like bleach, so I felt vaguely okay about being inside this box) I felt somewhat safe and secluded but still could head bop to the pounding of the bass to a wordless song. They played underground electronic music—super fitting for an event called Hot Mass.

"So, tell me," Brandon yelled over the music as he handed me my drink through the crawlspace hole we had to climb through to enter. "What's new with you? What's going on? What's up with your boyfriend? Tell me about him."

"Well," I laughed loudly to erase any unease in my voice. Everything felt so tender, painful, and guilt caked when I talked about James. "I'm single!" I laughed louder.

"Oh shit, I'm sorry. What happened?" Brandon asked.

"We just kind of… went in different directions. We weren't working out," I straight up lied, but it was easy with the void of light in this box and after chugging down another vodka mixed drink.

"That sucks. You seemed happy," he crossed his legs and sipped his drink.

"Yeah," the straw was still shoved in my mouth as I spoke. "Anyways, what about you? How's your boo?" I diverted the conversation far away from me.

"He's great! Working."

"I was going to ask why he didn't come tonight," I followed his lead and crossed my legs, too.

"Yeah, he wanted to, but he couldn't. He works most nights. His job kills him, I swear. Runs his ass to the bone."

We finished off our second drinks faster than the first ones. My inhibition fleeted like the flash of dance floor light in my eyes before quickly darting to another random corner of the room. "Let's go to the smoke room, honey. And get refills. We're empty."

"We really are alcoholics," I grumbled, hidden in forced laughter as all eyes darted to us struggling to crawl through the entryway to the main dance floor.

"Oh well," he brushed me away and led the way through the slow, beating pulse of the dance floor and the wall of light bulbs, brightening and dimming to the chorus of the song. Up at the DJ booth, a beautiful black woman with controlled-chaotic mini curls wore an angled fedora, hiding the rest of her hair underneath. Big headphones hung around her neck, with one of the muffs pressed firmly against her ear, as she bobbed up and down to the electric beat. She was feeling herself and the music. Everyone else kind of stood in the middle of the dance floor, staring at each other to see who they would try to pursue to make out with or take home once the sun started to rise. I wanted to make friends with the DJ, but I had an incredibly persistent stalker nonchalantly chasing me around with his sloppy button-up half pulled out of his pants and the stench of alcohol on his breathy cat calls.

My pursuer zoned on me almost immediately once Brandon and I appeared from our hiding spot. He was beyond thirsty, and I was the only oasis in this club—the only one he hadn't tried pursuing without a swift decline. Yet.

"Are you coming to the smoking room?" Brandon asked as we passed the bar area.

"Yeah, I'm going to get us refills. Be there in a second," I veered away from his lead and confidently strutted to the bar like I hadn't downed my last two vodka mixers in the last twenty minutes. "Two vodka Sprites, please," I asked the bartender, who eyed me up like I looked like a total Messica.

"Here," he slid the plastic cups along the uneven bar top and nodded to the tip jar.

"Thanks," I rolled my eyes and tipped him the money I was already going to put in there in the first place.

"Sup?" My Hot Mass stalker popped up behind a group of other sleekly dressed guys, hanging around the second floor opening of the stairwell.

"Hi." *Don't stop, keep going.*

"Single?" he looked over at the smoking room, referring to Brandon, no doubt.

"Completely," I stared directly into his eyes, hoping he would get uncomfortable and walk away. I would have walked away if someone did that to me, so obviously it would work on anyone, right?

"Cool," he looked over at the bar and the emptiness of his drink. He stepped by me to the bar, nodded to the bartender, who already had his drink coming. Totally not surprised you're well known in these parts, sir.

"What's in the drink?" I hesitantly asked as I sipped my own and stared at Brandon's.

"Tequila and ice," he didn't look at me when he talked, only sipped his order quickly and tossed his old cup in a giant garbage bag by the front of the bar.

"Nice," I looked up from my drink just in enough time to see him move in on me, put me against the wall, grab my face, and kiss me.

There was this episode in SpongeBob where, in his head, a million other SpongeBob minis were running around with everything catching fire for no reason in a raging panic. That was me in this exact moment. I tried to think of all the advice I was given about escaping uncomfortable or violating situations like this and I realized that I never was taught any of that as a guy. I wish I had been. It would have been useful in this moment, as this complete stranger made out with me, tongue touching my teeth, as I stood there in blinding, anxious panic. There wasn't an escape, though. I just had to ride it out as the bartender watched and gave zero fucks. Random make out sessions and dry humping and drunkenness and everything in between were normal culture here, and I was total victim to it.

Throw the drink on him, you idiot.

No, because then I'd get kicked out and ruin a fun night.

Is this even fun for you? Having a random stranger shove his tequila-washed tongue into your mouth against a wall in a club chalk-loaded with sex boxes and dark corners to disappear into?

We're having a good time, okay. This is fine. It happens to everyone in their life, yeah? Getting kissed by someone you don't want to be kissed by.

This is not normal. There is nothing normal about this. Stop trying to accept this as normal. It's wrong. Do something.

The man pushed his entire body onto me as I held out my hands to the side with both drinks in them, trying to make panicked noises so someone could stop this, but they only sounded pleasurable to him. I pushed my knee up and forward toward his body, slightly nudging him away so I could slip away toward the brighter lit smoking room where Brandon sat, talking to some other strangers.

"There you are! Did you get lost?"

"Long line at the——," I started to talk, but just shrugged and handed him his drink as my tongue became tingly and itchy and numbed like I was having some type of allergic reaction. It was probably all in my head. "Can we get more drinks?" I asked and left the overcrowded room. I felt like I might scream at the top of my lungs and embarrass myself.

"You okay?" Brandon asked as he downed the other drink.

"Yep," I continued to walk toward the bar, not even stopping to look at him. "Just having fun." I ordered three more vodkas for myself, straight, and one for Brandon.

"Two more on that, please. I need to stay on your level. Let's go dance!" he yelled as we downed three shots of vodka all at once at the bar and wiggled our way to the dancing crowd who swayed, jumped, and bobbed to the beat of the music (all dependent on how drunk they were). "Are you sure you're okay?" Brandon pressed.

"Yeah, why?" I slurred as the music shook my ribcage.

"You're acting—different, that's all!"

He followed my lead as we danced, and I ignored the rest of the conversation completely to let it die off into nothing but electronic bass and synth leads. Gated tones pumped up the drunken crowd as we all kind of mobbed together in one mess.

He found me again, somehow. His messy body pressed through the crowd that I drowned myself into, using it like a human shield, but he broke through the hot-bodied barriers I tried to hide within. He leaned over and kissed my neck right in front of Brandon, his eyes widening and edging me on to keep with this guy who I wanted nothing to do with. He didn't know, though, and the lights were too dim to see the absolute look of terror on my face as the vodka hit me like a wall of cement. My body temperature increased tenfold. This man's hands frisked up my body as he pulled me closer into him, within the mob of careless dancers, until his hands grabbed my ass. I leaned into him with every ounce of drunken strength I could muster to get him away from me, to hurt him, and darted through the sea of people encompassing Brandon and me. Brandon did a double-take and struggled to follow me to the stairwell as I stumbled down to the outside and into the fresh air. I was losing air quickly in this club and I needed out from everything and everyone. And that man. Whatever in the hell that was that happened.

"Vaughn, wait up!" Brandon yelled from the top of the stairs as I burst out of the glass door and stumbled toward my car. "What's going on?" his voice cut off when the club door slammed shut behind me.

"Hey there, stud," the bouncer smiled and nodded. The streetlights spun around and around in a million little circles as I breathed deeply in and out like a fish out of water, a fire out of air.

"Can we go in yet? What the hell?" some girl complained in the background as I put as much distance between me and the club as I could.

"Fucking damnit!" my hands slammed against the back of my car as I fumbled for the keys in my tight blue jean shorts.

"Hey bitch, what is going on with you?" Brandon drunkenly jogged toward the back of my car, where I walked away from and toward the driver side door.

"I couldn't breathe, I needed out of there. I have to work in the morning," I turned on my car and pressed all of the buttons in the center console until the air conditioning started blowing.

"Alright, that's fine, but can we sit here a moment to sober up? We shouldn't drive yet." He plopped down onto his seat and buckled up, "Is something wrong?"

"No, I'm just drunk and worried about work," I shrugged and stared at the speedometer until it almost blinded me.

"Okay," Brandon dropped his hands into his lap and looked around. "That guy in there really just attacked you. Was he your type?"

"No," I mumbled as my steering wheel dug into my forehead and imprinted. "Not at all," I clicked my tongue as feeling started to prickle back into it. I knew from New Orleans that I was allergic to tequila, but I didn't really realize that if I touched it at all I would start to itch and my throat would numb.

"I'm glad we're hanging out again, though. I miss our crazy nights at Cruze!" Brandon started dancing in his seat to no music.

"Me too! They were so much fun. So care-free," I sighed

and looked over at him.

"You know," he pulled on his seatbelt a little to tighten it against his body, "don't take this the wrong way, but you used to be such a force back then—so confident and unstoppable. You lost all that. You're different now. More reserved and quiet and internal." How he was speaking this clearly and real as drunk as we were was a mystery to me. Maybe it was me that was wasted, though. "What happened?"

Brandon never laid even a finger on me, but it felt like he punched me right in my stomach. I shrugged as I desperately tried to focus my vision before quickly leaning in and kissing him. His head jerked back a little, but his hand grabbed onto the back of my head and he kissed me back. The world didn't stop. Time kept going. My feelings intensified, but it was the liquor churning inside my stomach as I tried to keep it all down and inside of me, but my nerves set everything on fire and I couldn't keep it inside anymore. I pulled away from him, threw my head to the left as I opened the door, and blew chunks out onto the gravel parking lot underneath the one sodium light that illuminated half the lot.

The next morning, I showed up five hours late to work. I looked so terrible that my boss didn't even let me stay to make up time. He sent me away in shame with the same club clothes I wore from the night before and vomit-morning breath. My own stench choked me in my car as I drove through morning traffic back into Pittsburgh, where I knew my cat would be in my bed and I could sleep that entire shitty night away. Hell hath no fury like a messy, hungover gay spiraling out of control.

That drive back home marked an important end to a flash-in-a-pan era; the last clubbing night of my brief *youthful* phase. It was an era short-lived, but maybe that was all for good reason.

Chapter Seven
SUPERPOWER

I deserved that write up for my near no-call-no-show the morning following Hot Mass. It took a couple weeks to slip back into the good graces of the hotel but, nonetheless, I was able to redeem myself and slip quietly below the radar. Back when I was still at Starbucks as a barista trainer, I would engage in that kind of behavior all the time without even second guessing it. There was something about all the responsibility as an adult that we, somehow, unknowingly take on that wakes you up. Luckily for me, unlike many I know, I was given a second chance. It was time to put away the superhero costume and the wild nights out.

It was a Friday night after working two relentlessly brutal and exhausting weeks. Everything that could have gone wrong went wrong. The weekend before, I stayed at the hotel for emergency support because we had a new employee on overnight shifts and, at no fault of her own, she was clueless as to what she was doing. The general manager, Noah, and I finished work early that Friday and decided to treat ourselves with leaving work a little early, too.

"Want to go get a drink?" he asked as we walked out of the front door and into the cold December evening.

"After these past two weeks? Fuck yes," I scratched at my head underneath my beanie hat I wore to hide my balding. Two weeks was the longest I've gone since getting my hair buzzed by my dad. I refused to pay a barber twenty bucks to do something my dad could do with his clippers at home.

"Industry?" he asked, knowing well I'd say yes.

"You know it's always a yes for Industry."

Industry was only a two-minute drive from the hotel, give or take, depending on how the stoplights synchronized, and they made the next best Old Fashioned, after The Summit, of course.

"I'll buy," Noah offered, and I never said thank you. Unfortunately, and I'm totally ashamed about this, Noah liked to buy a lot of things for me and I lost my sense of gratitude in the meantime. I was at the incredibly ugly point of almost expecting him to buy drinks. I know, I know. It was a total asshole move on my part.

"Tequila for me and an Old Fashioned for him," he nodded toward me as I smiled at the waiter and set our menus aside. Murphy lights dangled from black cords, and out of rust-painted sconces across the walls, light as bright blues, whites, and yellows flashed on the parade of screens over the bar and across smaller walls. There was some type of sports game on the TVs.

"What a fucking week," I massaged the space where my eyebrows furrowed most days.

"I know," Noah laughed. "Thank God it's the weekend! Well, for me, at least."

"That's not funny. That's not funny at all, Noah." He made fun of the fact that I had a breakfast shift at six in the morning the next day. "After this shift, I'm off the next two days and I'm going to do nothing but stay in bed."

"Unless there is an emergency! Then your happy ass is coming right back into work," he smiled as he gulped down a mouthful of water.

"I think I would run into traffic. I'd die. Absolutely croak and stop breathing!" I mimicked crying and we both broke out into exhausted laughter.

"Gentlemen," the waiter came back lightning quick with our order, "Old Fashioned, and tequila for you, sir." He set them down and clapped his hands together, wanting to know if we were getting food.

"I can't. My dad's going to be home tonight, and I haven't seen him in literally weeks because of our work schedules," I bit the inside of my lip.

"I'm okay on food, too. Thanks," Noah handed the waiter our menus. "Can we get the check, too, please? It's a one and done night for us."

"Absolutely! Right on that," the waiter bowed out and walked over to the standalone kiosk adjacent to the bar where cherries, limes, and lemons sat lonely, in separate containers, for the bartenders to use as garnish.

"When can we fire Parys?" I asked as I took a huge gulp of the Old Fashioned and felt the burn radiate down into my bloated belly from our lunch earlier. "That homophobic bitch, I swear."

"Oh my!" Noah burst into a hardy laugh as he sipped his iced tequila shot. "Tell me how you really feel."

"Yeah, no really, though. She makes it so damn hard to hold my tongue!" I sipped the drink faster when I felt exhaustion prickling at the bottoms of my aching feet.

"You don't hold your tongue at all, Vaughn," Noah rolled his eyes as me and forced a laugh.

"It's because she's so rude! She purposefully makes my job harder and is the laziest person I've ever known," Exasperated, I breathed out of my nose. "I cannot stand her."

"I know, I know. She's so protected by corporate, though. Unless she wildly breaks protocol then I can't just fire her for nothing. Why don't you file a formal complaint against her?" he asked.

"I could, but my track record at the hotel isn't great," I mumbled.

"You only have one thing on there, Vaughn. Don't be so dramatic," Noah squeezed the lime in his mouth and swallowed quickly.

"I know, but still. I hate it. I feel like I have to make up for so much now. It's like I'm tainted or something," I looked over at the brick support where a television showed all the different available kegs they offered. In that split second, every ounce of my energy dropped down through the bottoms of my feet. My breath quivered, and my hands flashed with a wicked cold sweat that made me feel like I was going into some type of shock or that I was being electrocuted or that I was going to throw up. My vision tunneled as sound blurred rapidly.

"Vaughn?" Noah grabbed my hand and shook it, tumbling me back to reality. "Are you okay, buddy? You lost all the color in your face."

"So, I'm not imagining things then," I looked at him like a crazy person. I knew it by the way he looked so incredibly worried.

"What happened?" he forced a chuckle to break the incredible tension.

"I had the strongest déjà vu of my entire life. I've never felt something that strong before in my entire lifetime, Noah.

Holy shit," I pushed my seat away from the high-top table. "I'm sorry. I really need to go home. I'm not feeling too well."

"Of course, don't worry about it. Are you okay to drive? Do you need a ride home?" he asked.

"No, no. I'll be fine, I promise. I'll text you when I'm home, okay?" I flattened my lips into a forced smile and walked around the table to hug him. "Thanks for the drinks. I'll see you Monday or whatever."

I pulled on my black peacoat jacket and walked out of Industry without looking back. Cold air streamlined into my lungs as I breathed in deep to cool off my body from the sudden rush of warmth and heat. I don't know what happened in there, in that moment, when I quickly turned my head to look at a random brick support beam and the television on it, but it turned my stomach over—it made me feel incredibly small, helpless, and weak all at once.

"Please, Lord. Protect me on my drive home," I briefly prayed once I plopped into my car and started the fifteen-minute drive home in silence. I never drove in silence, ever. With every fiber of my being, I hated silence in vehicles. Whatever that feeling was, some type of cosmic strike through every single part of my body, frightened me more than anything. I was scared of the endless possible shockwaves that could follow after the body quake.

Chapter Eight
WONDERLESS BOY

Nothing crazy happened on my way home. Only a consistent, percolating panic attack that waited to happen at any moment as I drove five miles under the speed limit and made myself hyper aware of every car and light or sudden movement.

"Almost home, buddy boy?" Dad texted me as I merged into the turning lane off Banksville Road and toward home.

"Yep! I'm turning off Banksville now," I replied once I came to a full stop. Dad's truck was parked in his usual spot at the bottom of our street. We've always parked our vehicles there, ever since I could remember as a little kid. Char's car, his girlfriend who lived with us full-time, was parked on the cement pad—my spot before I moved out and she claimed it. It didn't really matter much to me because I parked right next to her in the gravel, but she really didn't drive well, so I worried about her ramming into my car when she arrived home after work, drunk or drugged up on cocaine.

"Oh, it's good to be home," I scratched the itching hair underneath my beanie, pressed snug. Dad stood, leaning against the living room window frame, with a huge smile when we locked eyes. He waved excitedly as I smiled and waved back, just as excited to see my dad. Once inside the basement door, the light already on for me when I got home, I threw my shoes off and changed into basketball shorts and a hoodie.

"There here is!" Dad sang as he did his signature dance—the lower half of his body doing the running man while his hands clapped in the air to the right of his head. "Mister America!"

"Hey Dad," I laughed as we embraced for the first time in two weeks. Since I stayed overnight last weekend, I hadn't seen him. I felt the long absence in my heart and soul—like a huge light was missing inside of me that was instantaneously turned on by simply being in the same room as him. "I missed you."

"You did?" he was surprised, but that didn't surprise me. I rarely reached out to him via text or phone call, ever, during the week. When I felt especially guilty about not replying to his phone calls or messages, I'd send a simple *"Love you"* so he knew I was thinking about him. "Are you hungry?" he asked as I followed him into the brightly lit kitchen.

"Starving," I pulled out the closest breakfast bar stool—I gotten them for his birthday—and slouched on the hard surface. Dad danced over from the stove to the barren pantry. Neither of us had been home in days, so, of course, there wasn't any food. Char was the only one home almost ever, and Lord knows she didn't stock the house with food. She used to in the beginning, when she first moved in, but not now that she'd secured her spot in the house.

"I only have mac 'n cheese. I'm sorry," he looked down, disappointed at the sparse selection to choose from.

"Honestly, Dad, I'd love mac 'n cheese after this horrible week," I laughed as he brought out the milk and butter from the fridge.

"You're about to get the best mac 'n cheese boxed dinner you've ever had."
He filled the pots we'd had since I was a little kid with water and used his lighter to ignite the burner.

"I can't wait," I sighed and slipped off the chair to make myself a drink.

"Why was your week so bad? Everything okay at work?" he stirred in the noodles before the water boiled.
I never questioned my dad's techniques because he could literally make food peeled off a hot street corner by a city garbage can taste like the best steak you've ever had in your entire life. He had some type of magical cooking power that I was graciously granted only a little sliver of.

"The assistant general manager at work really chaps my ass. She genuinely does not like me and makes my job so much harder than it already is."

"Well, you have to make sure you respect them anyways. You'll always find someone to hate at a workplace. That's just how things work, buddy."
I loved my dad more than anything, but one thing that always got under my skin was when he went on these lecture kicks, like I was in the wrong. Parys was a genuine bitch, and I knew my dad only wanted me to see it from a different perspective, but sometimes, his lectures were a little overkill when all I wanted to do was complain for three seconds.

"I know. I respect her, Dad. She just makes me want to scream sometimes, I swear," I scratched at hair growing like a wrap around my head, with the most baldness on top. Dad and I were both cursed with terrible hair genetics, but at least we both had nicely shaped heads for when we decided to shave. I wasn't quite there yet and stuck to wearing hats all the time. It was an embarrassing thing to not have beautiful hair as a gay man. Anything skewed with body or image, for gay men, was taboo and hidden with a bunch of surface level cover ups.

"Good," he stirred the macaroni as he swallowed loudly.

"I won't eat that entire box. You can have some, too, if you're hungry," I bit at my fingers as he stirred and readied the metal colander.

"No, Char wants to go grab a sub for dinner. I'm fine," Dad moved the pot of noodles toward the sink where the metal colander sat inside the tan ceramic tub. He rounded off a couple jokes he'd tested out on his coworkers throughout the week and had me nearly rolling out of my chair laughing so hard. Dad always had this incredible sense of humor and quick-wittedness that I wish I had more of. Being around him, I learned his humor via some weird osmosis, but he was wildly faster and funnier than me. He always threatened me that once he started making me laugh, he could finish me off and have me laughing so hard I'd cry and fall over. I always dared him to! Every time, he'd quickly decline and change the subject.

"Hey, I hate to be a bother since you already made me food and you're going out to eat in a minute, but can you buzz my head before you leave?" I'd already prepped my response for if he declined.

"Sure, bud," Dad smiled as he filled my bowl to the top with golden mac before walking into the bathroom to get his clippers and a towel. "I'll be downstairs when you're ready for the cut, alright?"

"Sweet! Thanks, Dad," I dug into my dinner, barely even tasting any of it as I swallowed big spoonful after spoonful of cheese powder-flavored noodles.

Dad and I called it our "laundry room therapy" when he'd cut my hair in the laundry room downstairs. Our basement was partially finished with walls of faded drywall Dad started to fix when I was a little kid, before the great divorce. Down the stairs to the basement from the main living floor, a giant wooden waterbed frame sat above a light wood desk he'd used for mail and drawing at one point in time. When I was a kid, there were times he'd spend all day down there. One reason being the basement was always cool, no matter the season. It was partially underground— you know, the classic Pittsburgh basement equipped with a Pittsburgh bathroom. I always considered ours to be the fanciest Pittsburgh bathroom, though. Not only did it have the toilet, but it also had walls, a door, *and* a shower.

Mostly, since I'd usually complain about work beforehand, it was Dad's turn to complain about anything that happened the past week away at work. This time, it was about a coworker who bought an assault rifle and brought it to work, but who wouldn't change his underwear or bathe or anything like that. Some of the coworkers Dad complained about worried me a lot when I'd think about him hanging over the edge of a bridge, inspecting it with them in the dolly, too. What if they go off? Then what? It'd be the end of everything. Sharp stinging shook me back to reality as he ran the clippers across my neck and up through the hair that would grow.

"Sorry, buddy," he rubbed an area where he caught skin on my neck. "Got you a bit. It's not bleeding badly. You're fine."

It took years of practice, but I learned to never react when he clipped me because he'd feel so bad about it and it would absolutely tank his mood. We were having such a great night catching up—no need to let a little knick end it here.

"It's fine, Dad. I barely felt a thing," I laughed.

"You're lying, but that's okay," he laughed through his nose as I smiled at a pile of towels in front of the washer and dryer inches away from me. Orange light from the one streetlight on our steep hill bled across the wet and leafless branches in our yard. "Almost done," he hummed *Plush* by Stone Temple Pilots as he rounded my ears to finish our therapy session. "You're good to go," he pulled the towel he used to cover my neck, even though I was going to shower afterward anyways. "Looking good, Bobby." Bobby was one of twelve nicknames he called me. It kind of progressed throughout my life, the first being "Lunchmeat" when I was born since, and I quote, "You were like a little pound of lunchmeat I could hold in my one arm."

"Thanks again. I appreciate you cutting it before you leave," I went to hug him.

"Nope, nope. You're covered in little hairs. I can't be out and all itchy. It'll drive me nuts," he laughed and pointed to the doorway to the upper floor where our main bathroom was. "Are you going to be home later?"

"Yeah, I work at six in the morning. I'm not going anywhere," I snuck by him and picked up a clean towel off of the brown couch where Dad sat to fold all of the laundry.

"I'll see you later then," he clapped on my back.

"I'll be here!" I turned and smiled at him before I retreated to the bathroom to shower the little itchy hairs and the day away. "I love you. Glad you're home."

"I love you too, buddy. It's good to be home and see you," Dad hugged me anyways and let me retreat upstairs with a fresh towel and a new bar of Irish Spring soap.

I was in bed within forty-five minutes of first getting into the shower. I didn't put on any music and enjoyed the silence of the house. When Dad was home or when he was away, and it was just Char, they'd leave the televisions on almost all day. That, or Dad would pick up one of his guitars and sing for hours until his voice was hoarse. My phone vibrated as I ran through the house to the forest green carpeted stairwell that led to our bedrooms.

"Come over and play cards," a good friend of mine, Andrew, sent me a message.

"I work so early tomorrow. And it's a far drive. I really can't tonight," I flash texted back.

"Come on, please. I have rum and Dr. Pepper, and you can stay here and go to work from here tomorrow," he was very enticing, but I had stipulations for coming over I needed to put into place before I agreed, so another Hot Mass wouldn't occur.

"Fine, but I need to be in bed by no later than midnight, alright?" I responded.

"Yay! Okay."

I hesitantly rolled off the bed and packed a bag of cleanish work clothes for the night, a toothbrush, and some deodorant for the morning. There was nothing worse than sweating all day, checking rooms at work, and smelling unpleasant.

For the first time all day, I blasted music to wake me up on the way to Andrew's house out in the middle of nowhere-Rochester. He lived on a cute little farm with his mom and boyfriend where he ran his own horse-training business and had a few goats. When I arrived at the A-frame home, warmly lit by string lights inside the loft area, he waited by the door for me, drink in hand.

"I'm telling you, I need to go to bed and wake up on time," I rolled my eyes at him and pressed my car button twice to lock it up for the cold night.

"I don't know about getting up because you know your ass

that I'm next to dead when I sleep, but I'll make sure you go to bed earlier than I do," Andrew hugged me as I fended off his two adorable dogs who loved to give kisses. His friend that lived up the road was there, but his boyfriend had already gone to sleep since he didn't drink and didn't like to be around alcohol.

We were able to get through three rounds of whatever card game we were playing before it was time for me to go to sleep. Responsibly, I hugged them both and said goodnight, so I wouldn't be a zombie in the morning while serving breakfast to a team of youth hockey players.

"We really need to hire a breakfast attendant, Noah. I'm getting tired of the breakfast shifts," I texted him before I curled up into the spare bed by the front of the loft, but he didn't respond. It was 12:01 a.m., and the last time I looked at my phone before ending the full-hearted night at the end of a miserably draining week.

My phone exploded with sound as I reached over, exhaustion mounting on top of me like an unbearable weight.

"Hello?" I mumbled half-in-half-out of sleep.

"Vaughn, where are you?" they asked.

"I'm in bed, what are you talking about?" I heard Andrew on the other side of the line as I hung up on him.

Another ring jerked me back into my semi-sleeping state.

"Vaughn, listen to me. I—need help," they yelled on the phone.

"Andrew, are you locked out of the house or something or what? I have work in the morning. I need to be sleeping," my anger flared at how exhausted I was.

"No, Vaughn," they sobbed as they spoke over the phone

in sloppy words that I barely could make out. "This is Char. This isn't your friend. This is Char. Listen to me. Your dad is dead."

"I really need to go to sleep. I have work early in the morning," I wiped the drool from my mouth and rolled over onto my phone so I didn't have to hold it against my ear.

"Why do you keep telling me this?" she cried harder. "Listen to what I'm saying!" Char screamed through the phone until her voice cracked in a shaken sob. "Your dad is dead!"

She woke me. I don't know how many times she had to sob and scream it over the phone until I snapped out of my heavy sleep, but I was up and aware at that moment. I felt everything all at once, like a bucket of cold water doused me, soaked through my clothes, and into my pumping veins.

"Wait, what?" I jumped up from the mattress on the floor and stared into the corner of the room, at a pillow covered by a photograph of a horse, shoved on top of a bunch of stuffed animals.

"It's Char! Your dad is dead, you need to come home! Your dad is dead," she repeated. "Your dad is dead. He died, he's gone," she cried harder as she got farther away from the phone.

"Hel—hello?" a man's voice I'd never heard before came through the phone.

"Who is this?" I asked as I yanked my phone cord out from the wall and stuffed it in my backpack.

"This is Char and your dad's friend, Little Angelo."

"I'm on my way home. I'll be there in forty-five minutes, okay?" I didn't care who he was, nor did I know who that man was. I'd never heard Dad talk about a Little Angelo, but I surely didn't want to talk on the phone. I needed to get home. That's all that mattered.

Down the two flights of stairs to where we played cards,

Andrew and his friend were still up listening to music and flipping cards.

"What's wrong?" he asked.

"I think—," I knew what I needed to say, but something stopped me from saying it. Maybe if it wasn't spoken out into the Universe it would reverse what had already happened. "I think my dad just died." I turned away, smashed down the backs of my gray shoes and ran out the door without closing it behind me or looking back to see if they followed.

Maybe he was being revived and Char jumped the gun? She was never the brightest bulb in the pack. She had to be wrong. Dad isn't dead. He always told me he would outlive me to at least one hundred years old.

Dad isn't dead.

No, that's—no, Dad isn't dead.

Char is wrong.

My phone rang as I spun out in the driveway. My sister, Chelsey, called me.

"Look, I don't know what's going on," I didn't let her speak, "but I'm on my way home now. It'll take me forty-five minutes to get there, less if I speed, but I can't talk on the phone right now, okay?"

"Alright, buddy," I could hear her holding back sobs on the phone to keep me calm. She tried so hard, but I knew when something was wrong with her. I always had, even if she felt she hid it so well from the world. Chelsey could never hide her pain from me. "I love you," her voice shook.

"I love you, too," I hung up and threw my phone onto the passenger seat.

I looked at the clock: 12:32 a.m.

It really happened. My dad was dead.

A THOUSAND WAYS TO DIE IN SIX MONTHS

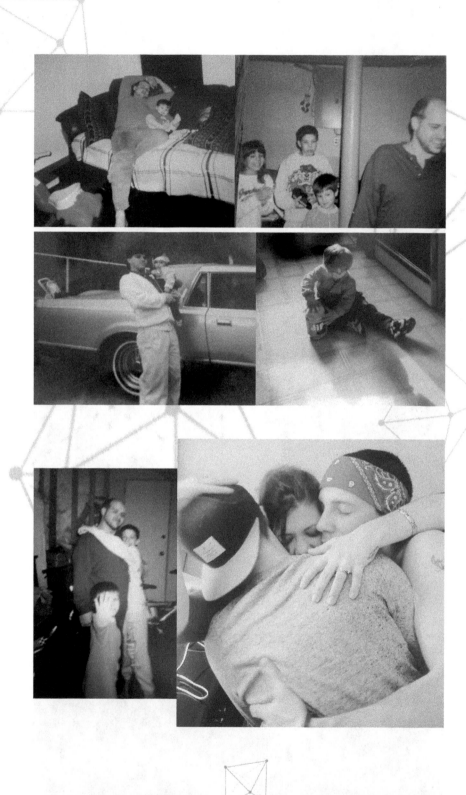

Chapter Nine
THREE HOURS

"Noah, my dad died. I need you to get to my house," my hands trembled uncontrollably as I impatiently sat at the last red light before the highway back into town.

"Jesus Christ," he replied just as the light turned green. "I'm on my way."

I plugged my phone into the charger and set it in the middle console instead of throwing it on the seat. Rubber spun as I turned the wheel hard right and entered the highway. Bright highway lights flashed past faster and faster through the sunroof above.

This was where I lost control.

Seventy-five, eighty, ninety, then one-hundred miles per hour flashed on the heads-up display against the windshield. Cars blurred past me as I drove erratically down the highway faster than anyone ever should. Watching the road didn't interest me. Safety of other drivers on the highway didn't interest me. Looking out for cops or the threat of getting pulled over didn't make me slow down. I wanted them to come after me. Why? Who knows. Maybe it was so I wasn't alone in that moment. Everything ached with a dark fragility I'd never felt before. Stories fabricated of how he died over and over again until I screamed and slammed into the steering wheel in a guttural cry that cracked when it burst from my throat.

Death was an option.

You could do it. Close your eyes and let go of the steering wheel. It would be quick like the bright flash before a light bulb burns out.

Was it quick for Dad? Did he get shot at the bar Char worked at? He had some enemies, but I don't think any who would want to kill him. Was it a car accident? Were they drinking? Char sounded drunk on the phone. She was hard to understand through all of her sobbing. How are my sister and brother there already? How long did they wait to tell me? I screamed louder, over and over again, above the Christian song I played that really only made me sad instead of hopeful. I prayed. I prayed hard, because that was what you did as a crisis-Christian, yeah? You prayed to God for peace and hope—for miracles that would never happen unless lightning struck. *You won't be given a miracle because you doubt the possibility of God bringing back the dead. You might as well have been the one to murder your own father.*

Clouds swirled and covered the top of Pittsburgh's illuminated skyline as I sped down I-579 into town. I passed under and over bridges that my dad would never hang underneath ever again; through tunnels we'd never again drive through on our way back home from my uncle and aunt's house in North Versailles. There wasn't an inch of the city that wasn't engraved with the memory of Dad and me at some point in our lives. I mustered quick flashes of those memories in a manic attempt to remember all of them, and they charged through my brain like a thousand volts of electricity, discharging all at once: when he took me to Mr. Magoo's up on Mt. Washington as a little kid, or our kayaking excursions along the Allegheny River, and when he'd take me to work, or cut grass for the church our family attended a few times before.

I had this drawer inside my head that looked like one of my parents' nightstands—the ones they used to have in their room when we were a family—where I'd store all the hard things I went through and couldn't deal with all at once. It allowed me to control the uncontrollable emotional parts that felt impossibly large to even think about handling. That drawer made things accessible to handle, and with the violent blow of losing my dad three hours after I saw him, I tried to stuff those soft memories inside it to preserve them, like old cassette tapes or family scrapbooks. I didn't know what was going to happen when I arrived home, how much I'd lose or have to shove in that drawer, if there would be blood splattered in our home or his body still inside. I knew nothing of what to do or how to act or when to cry or what to say to my family waiting for me.

"Almost home, buddy boy?" Dad texted me as I merged into the turning lane off Banksville Road and toward home.

"Yep! I'm turning off Banksville now," I replied once I came to a full stop.

The red and blue flashing emergency lights glowed all the way down the street from Banksville Road when I merged into the turning lane. There were cops everywhere on my street. The coroner's truck was parked diagonally on the side of our steep hill with a police car parked in front of and behind it. My brother, Brian, and Chelsey waited at the top of the city steps where the cement branched off onto the walkway that led to the many entrances of our home. Dad would have flipped if he came home to the house lit up like a Christmas tree, with every light on in the house. Chelsey's husband waited next to her, his arm wrapped loosely around her, while all three of them smoked cigarettes.

"Keep your shit together," I hoarsely mumbled as I wiped my eyes dry and collected myself.

It felt like I found the lever to my feelings and kicked the nob off to dry the well cracked inside my chest. I didn't want to look over at my neighbor's house to see if they might be watching and whispering. I knew they were, and I was embarrassed about what was happening and what I couldn't control—not because my dad was dead, but because they would feel sorry for me. Everyone stared at me, even the stars stared, as I walked across the night-cloaked street to the bottom of the city steps, to what I'd find up these steps I'd climbed an infinite number of times. This time was different, though. Like there were weights attached to my feet that dragged below water while I tried to trek against the current.

"Hey bud," Chelsey puffed her cigarette one last time and threw it onto the street as the ember of the cigarette ignited quickly and scattered ash across the cobblestone hill where it struck.

"Hi," I answered a bit shakier than I anticipated as she pulled me into her so my head rested down on her shoulder. My sister is shorter than me, but she gives the best hugs. That was what I needed to handle whatever was coming next.

"Hey," Brian pulled me into him next and squeezed until my breath was pushed out of my lungs in a weakened wheeze.

"Hi," I repeated. "What's going on?"

"They're in the basement with Dad now," Chelsey nodded to the basement door that hung wide open. There were cops everywhere, and one undercover cop, dressed like a gentleman, smoking a cigar, that guarded the basement door like a hawk.

"Are we allowed inside?" I asked.

"Not yet, no. Not until they're finished photographing," Chelsey shivered and leaned into her husband, David.

"Photograph... never mind," I waved the question away once it clicked why they were photographing. "Has anyone called Mom?" I asked.

"No one can get a hold of her. The phone's off," Brian lit another cigarette.

"Typical. Never there when you need her to be," Chelsey rolled her eyes as her voice shook. She turned into David's chest as she quietly cried into his worn, grey graphic T-shirt. Usually, I would correct her negative talk about our mom, but this wasn't the time or place.

"A friend of ours that lives near your mom is going to wake her up now," David whispered as Chelsey cried into him, hard. I stared at every police officer's face that passed us in hopes they'd recognize me as his son and tell me anything about what happened. None of them even glanced, only kept their head down and eyes to the ground.

"Okay, thanks," a wailing sound echoed from the side of the house where the light wouldn't touch. "What in the hell is that?"

"Oh my goodness," Brian scratched his head as he exasperatedly looked away from the house.

"That—*bitch*—hasn't stopped screaming since we got here."

"Hey, you guys, all these cars can't be in the driveway," my neighbor yelled from her wooden porch as she smoked a cigarette.

"Are you *fucking kidding me?*" Chelsey went off like a makeshift explosive. "Our dad died! It's fucking passed midnight! You don't have anything going on, so shut up and just go back into your house and mind your own damn business!" She pointed toward her with her cigarette holding hand as the smoke snaked into the chilly night. My neighbor didn't know what was going on, so I don't blame her. Also, I'm kind of non-conflict, so I calmed Chelsey down and walked away from the three of them standing there.

Some older woman held Char up when she saw me and started collapsing onto the ground. I jogged toward both women and helped her up as she tried everything she could to fall down onto the ground.

"Oh, Vaughn!" I'm not exaggerating when I said she wailed like a banshee. "I'm so sorry!" Char tried to stand with her shaky legs and cigarette in her right hand and one of my dad's bandanas in the other. "I can't believe this. I just can't believe this!" Char cried harder.

"It's life. It happens," I struggled to hold her up as the short man that guarded the basement door watched from afar. It felt weird hearing myself sound so disconnected. Char left no room for emotional destruction right now; it was all anyone could afford with the state she was in. "What happened?" I asked.

"I don't know. We were getting ready for bed and—," she started wailing again and couldn't spit out her sentence. "We were just going to bed and he went downstairs to change and—"

"Okay," I let her friend take over holding Char up and stepped a couple feet back from her because I wasn't going to let her be this dramatic. They weren't married. It was my dad. He only kept her around because he was lonely and I wasn't home all the time.

"Can we go inside yet, or?" I turned to the man guarding the door.

"Oh, I don't know. I'm not the cops," he shrugged his shoulders and breathed in deep through his partially smoked cigar.

"Okay?" I held my hand out toward him. "Well, can you go

ask? It's freezing and I'm not staying outside until they're done. Can we go into the kitchen or something?"

"I'll… ask," he hesitated as he walked into the basement where they were photographing Dad's body. "Yeah, you can go—"

"Come on," I waved over at my siblings as we trekked up the side cement steps along our multicolored brick house to the back entrance into the kitchen. The frigid breeze cycled from the open basement door to the upstairs in a powerful draft that chilled me down to my bones. Everything looked ordinary. Part of me expected the house to be trashed in some type of argument gone awry, like in the Investigation Discovery shows Dad always watched. Leftover mac 'n cheese sat untouched and crusted to the bottom of the black paint chipped pot he used to make it in. The light felt less warm on my body, the texture of our beige carpet sharper than a measly three hours ago, and the bamboo green paint on the walls seemed less vibrant and more dried and dead looking. My house even smelled less like Dad—more of a cigar and snow smell than bar soap and wood.

"Has anyone called Aunt Mar yet?" I looked at both my siblings and tried to search for Char, but she was nowhere to be seen.

"Not yet," Brian bit down tensely so his jaw bones pushed out from underneath his skin.

"I'll call, I guess," I said.

"I can do it, buddy," Brian pulled out his cellphone and started searching through his contacts.

"No, it's fine. Let me do it. I'll be right back," I searched for my phone and walked from the breakfast table I'd eaten at only three hours ago, through the pantry, and into the bathroom. I shut the bathroom door as much as I could—it was warped from years of shower steam and moisture—and sat on the wooden toilet seat.

I hit the green call button but hung up before the dial tone even beeped once. "Come on," I dropped my head into my hands and thought of how I'd say it out loud—how it would sound as my lips formed the words and spoke them into the universe in a permanency that I'd never get back. *"Fuck."*

"Hello?" she sounded a little buzzed. It was a Friday night after all. Well, Saturday morning.

"Hey Aunt Mar, it's Vaughn," I slid off the toilet and knelt over the seat, lifting it up when the nausea took over and threatened to projectile vomit rum, soda, and tortilla chips everywhere.

"What's going on? Is everything alright?" she asked.

"N—no," I breathed in deeply. "Everything isn't alright."

"What happened?" Mar asked, but I couldn't talk. I couldn't breathe or think or even blink. I was frozen and floating inside some space between reality and the imaginary inside my head. I thought about a million different, terrible places that I'd read about in books or that were real, places I thought about wanting to exist in, instead of inside this bathroom—this bathroom that I'd studied every corner of over the years, where I'd cried a million times in dark showers over heartaches, where I'd experienced my first foodborne illness from a hotdog at a church picnic. *Anywhere, but here, please.*

"Vaughn, what's going on? Are you going to tell me or what?" her impatience pierced through the phone and brought me back.

I took one deep breath, used the toilet seat to pull myself up from the floor, and sat back down to stare at the broken angel statues across the toilet from years of accidentally punching them right off the ledge when we'd dry ourselves off after a shower.

"Dad died," it fell out of my mouth so low even I wasn't sure if I actually said it or not.

"No," Aunt Mar started crying instantaneously, "no, no, no, you're fucking with me."

"I'm sorry," I should have cried. I wanted to cry, but I let that beast out when I was driving home alone.

"Oh my God, honey, I'm so sorry. Oh shit," she struggled to keep her composure over the phone. "I can't talk right now. Are you alone? Are you okay? Do you know what happened?"

"I'm fine, I'm not alone. The police are here taking photos. They haven't said anything yet. I'll let you know when I know anything."

"Alright. You keep me updated. I'm coming over tomorrow morning, okay? You hang in there, honey. Have you told the others?" I knew Aunt Mar meant my other aunts and uncle and my grandmother.

"No, you're the first."

"Don't worry about telling them. I will do it, okay? I've got to go now. I love you so much," she hung up the phone.

"I love you, too," I mumbled and shoved my phone into my pocket. There was a white angel trapped underneath an upside-down glass globe that waved back and forth around the opening. It was an angel I'd made years ago, right after my parents divorced, and I've seen it in the same place so many times that I hadn't even thought about that static time for our family in years. I thought about what it would take to go back and tell an incredibly naïve and younger Vaughn that life is going to nosedive deep one day, and you need to listen to your dad more.

Now? You're unprepared. You're weak. Everything you took for granted, became familiar and comfortable with, has been stripped away in three hours, and now you have no other choice but to break.

Chapter Ten
GUARANTEES OF LIFE

I didn't waste time in the bathroom after our phone conversation and gathered with my family in the kitchen. Every couple seconds, I could hear the camera click in the basement, some mumbled words, and then more clicks from the camera. Char still sobbed outside, beyond consolable, as her friend harshly attempted to calm her down and talk her off the mental ledge.

"Hi," her friend looked over at the darkness around the corner.

"Hi?" Noah's voice perked my ears as I walked to go retrieve him so he wasn't caught in the mess outside.

"In the kitchen," I called to him as he appeared around the corner in what he was wearing at work earlier that day. He smelled like liquor and I immediately didn't want him there, but a bigger part of me was glad he made it okay and that someone outside of my family was with me. Without another word, I walked into him and we hugged.

"I'm sorry," Noah spoke above my head, I fit perfectly underneath his chin.

"Yeah," I spoke into his chest as we stood out in the cold, dark walkway that wrapped completely around my house.

Sorry. I hated the word "sorry." Any other stock expression of grief or sorrow or condolence was just as distasteful to me. I knew they meant well, anyone who said it, but it just felt like words weren't enough. Not even for me. Noah and I walked into the house and shut the door to stop the cigarette smoke that Char and her friend blew out from entering the house. It already smelled weird enough. I didn't want cigarette smoke in there. Dad would have flipped shit if his house smelled like cigarette smoke. Sometimes, when it was really cold, she'd smoke right out of the window of their bedroom and the smoke would leak through the vents and choke me out in my own bedroom. It pissed me off more than anything. Especially with Char.

We quietly stood around the kitchen and said nothing. Everyone stared at their feet or pressed their lips together to form a really sad and smug smile. *Click, click, click.* Dull white flashes burst onto the top of the basement stairwell wall that Dad painted blood orange years ago. He never painted over it when he repainted the entire dining and living room. My phone vibrated in my sweatpants pocket and snatched my attention away from the flashing.

"Hello?" I called out.

"What's going on, baby?" Mom sounded out of breath and was crying. "Are you okay? What are you doing?"

"I'm fine, Mom. Just please, if you're driving, be careful. I already lost one parent. I don't need to lose another one, okay? Get here safe and I'll see you soon."

"I love you so much, sweetie. I'm so sorry. I'll be safe, gonna get off the phone. See you soon."

"I love you too, Ma," I hung up the phone and pressed down

on the home button to unlock it. In the top four conversations I had in the last three hours, Dad's was there. I opened it and started speed scrolling up so I wouldn't read anything, but I wanted to see how far back I had between him and me. "What?" I whispered so no one else could hear me. *Four months.* Only four months of texts were saved in my phone. The rest of our conversations, I'd never get back, totally wiped. *Why in the flying fuck would you delete your conversations?* "Damnit."

"What?" Chelsey looked over at me from her husband's chest.

"Nothing," I waved. "My phone's being stupid," I clicked down at the bottom of the screen to speed scroll back to the most recent text messages between us.

Hey Dad! Just wanted to let you know I'm safe and staying over a friend's house tonight. Going to work from here. I'll see you after work! Love you. Sent at 11:57 p.m.

"What the fuck is he doing?" Chelsey leaned over to Brian so she could talk low and unheard.

"I don't know," Brian scowled at the man that was dressed like an undercover cop, holding his lit cigar in his hand and smoking it without a care in the world in my dining room. Just like cigarettes, Dad would have gone ballistic if anyone smoked in the house. *Anything.* Yet this random man stood in my home and lit up without a thought in the world that it might not be okay to do that. Everything smelled like his foul cigar—sweet leather and gin.

"Aren't you going to say anything?" my sister whispered closer to our brother's chest.

"No? That isn't my call. It's Vaughn's call. It's his house."

This was not my house. This was Dad's house. It always would be Dad's house, even after he died. I put no effort or time or money into this home. How was it my call to make this man stop smoking in it? Yeah, Dad would have beat his head in for the level of disrespect going on right now, but this wasn't my house at all.

This is your house. You'll always have this place to come home to. I heard Dad in my ear, clear as day, when he'd come home a little buzzed and tell me how proud he was of me and what an amazing young man I was becoming. I won't ever be sitting in my bedroom, playing video games, and him come home from work, riding his motorcycle, or from being out and have his long-winded speeches about how proud he was of me and how he knew I'd do great, great things. Quickly, before I forgot, I shoved it into the drawer inside my head, locked away for safe keeping.

"I don't really care," I shrugged before I leaned onto the counter.

"You heard him," Brian sighed.

"Really, Vaughn? Come on now. You know Dad would have killed him if he saw him smoking in this house. You don't like smoke. I know you don't," she pleaded.

"I know that, but what am I supposed to do? I don't even know who in the hell he is or why he's here."

"Do you want me to do it?" Chelsey pulled away from her husband as I saw the deepest flicker of anger inside her eyes. "I will if you want me to."

"Yeah, I do."

What I really wanted was to not be the bad guy and avoid all confrontation. Otherwise, I'd implode if another stir happened here tonight with everything else that was going on.

"Okay," my sister walked up to the short man who paced through the house and looked at the few pictures we had as well as some decorative pieces Dad got from his mission trip in Haiti years ago. "Hey dude," she pointed angrily at him, "get that fucking cigar out of this house."

"What?" he seemed surprised.

"You heard me," she yelled louder. "Don't smoke that in here. If my dad was alive, he'd beat your ass if he caught you smoking in his home."

"I'm you dad's friend, Little Angelo, alright? We go way back."

"I really don't give a shit who you are! You're going to put out that damn cigar."

"Are you serious? You're going to make me put out this twenty dollar cigar?"

"Go smoke it outside, dude. You're being crazy," David chimed in as my brother stirred in his spot from the excitement. He was getting angry, and I felt the pressure building inside this house so quickly that all I wanted to do was light a match and end it all. "Don't need to be an asshole about it, alright? Just go and smoke your cigar outside."

"No, I'm not smoking this outside. I'll just toss this twenty-dollar cigar out the window and make everyone happy, yeah? Is that what yinz want?" he pranced through the kitchen toward the back door.

"Really, if it's that big of a deal, I'll give you the twenty dollars myself so you can go buy another one of your cheap cigars," Brian started yelling at him.

"Can you not right now?" I begged.

"Forget it," he tossed his cigar with an angry flick of his fingers. "It's over and done with, alright?" He argued like an Italian—mumbled his frustrations over and over again, loud enough so they could be heard and push buttons, but perceived low enough like it wasn't all on purpose.

"Don't be a prick, man, jeeze," David walked over into the

dining room and consoled my sister as she sat down on one of our old dining room chairs and held her head in her hands.

I escaped passed the dining room and into the lightless living room, stopping just shy of the window I saw my dad stand in front of hours ago, waving excitedly at my arrival home. It felt false. Everything felt wrong and distant and ghostlike; almost as if I was cycling through a View-Master, clicking through the images, one by one, in an endless cycle. A thin layer of dust covered the entertainment stand we'd had in the house since I was born. The same black cassette and multi-disc changer sat underneath my black gaming console, and above that, the cable box—I knew if I turned it on that it would be set to the Investigation Discovery channel.

"Vaughn?" my mom called out to me as the kitchen door opened.

"Hey," I walked over to the kitchen to meet her. Our eyes locked as she held her purse loosely in her hand, shoulder strap dangling close to the ground, wearing her lighter pair of jeans and a light olive colored shirt that was nowhere warm enough for December. The second most vivid memory I have of that night was the look in her red eyes. She had been crying, I could tell. I saw her cry hundreds of times before. But the way she looked at me with her reddened eyes, eyebrows bridged close together, and mouth lines showing—she looked at me like I was damaged, not like damaged goods, but like I was carrying inconsolable damage. It was like she looked at her little boy, going onto the front lines of the battlefield, or coming home from the painful aftermath of war. I know she wanted to take all of the pain away. She would take it all on as her own if she could, without even hesitating for a second. But we aren't superheroes, and life doesn't allow for the sacrificial bartering of pain, grief, or loss.

Unlike time, loss was the only thing we were guaranteed in our lifetime. So I hugged my mom like it was the last time I'd ever hug her.

Chapter Eleven
REAL

Everyone outside squeezed their way onto the main floor all at once. Cold December air blanketed the house, but it was so incredibly cramped and stuffy that I felt my panic in high tide slam against the dunes I'd built around myself. Everyone talked all at once, or at least I thought they did, and argued, and Char still sobbed uncontrollably.

"Listen," I pulled her aside in the living room to the wooden landing at the bottom of the stairwell that led to our bedrooms.

"Mhmm?" Char wiped her eyes, streaked with clumped mascara.

"I know this is hard right now. The most unimaginable thing for both of us happened. I don't understand why it happened, but we both lost someone we loved. I mean this in the gentlest way possible, you need to pull it together for two seconds and tell me what happened."

Char looked so broken, even in the shadowed stairwell. Chelsey peered over at me while Char had her back to my sister. If Chelsey could shoot knives out of her eyes, Char would've been dead by now. My not-so-pep talk didn't work, and she started crying all over again. I skipped stairs, just like I'd always practiced as a kid, and fell onto my bed in my room. The seam of my sheets felt sharp against my fingertips as I skimmed down them until my arm couldn't stretch any further.

"Can you come upstairs, please?" I texted my mom.

"On my way," she replied as I heard her slowly trek up the forest green carpeted stairwell. "What's going on?" she sat on the bed next to me and held my hand.

"I can't have all these people here. I'm going to scream. They need to leave or I'm genuinely going to have a meltdown— between Char excessively crying and the tension between all these random people inside my house and cops in the basement, everyone that isn't family or Char needs to go."

"Alright, I'll tell them!" Mom sprung right into action.

"No, wait. I'll do it. You don't have to do that," I hugged her tightly before she followed me downstairs to the main floor. "Everyone that is not family or Char needs to leave. It's too much and too many people. I don't care where you go, whether it's out-side or what, but you're not going to be inside this house. Got it? Good."

I walked back into the living room and sat down where my mom followed. Noah uneasily walked into the living room and leaned against the wall.

"I'm sorry I made you drive all the way out here. Are you okay to drive?" I asked.

"Yeah, no, I'm fine. I promise. Don't be sorry, I appreciate you calling me," he held out his arms for a hug. We embraced for longer than a couple of seconds as I pushed my face into his chest. I felt like an asshole. I didn't want to add feeling like an asshole to the list of a million other things that rushed into my brain and felt across every part of my body. There was a limit I felt myself almost pass; a limit that I couldn't come back from. If I breached through the barrier, I could never reach gravity again.

"I'm calling off from work," I groaned.

"I assumed so," he laughed and headed for the door. "Call me if you need anything, okay?"

"I will," I watched as Noah snaked through Char's friends while they scowled at me like I was a heartless person. Some parts of me believed them. I felt heartless. Char showed more grief than I did. What those assholes didn't know, though, is that none of my grief is surface grief. This is my fight response. "Sorry to make them leave," I called to Char.

"Don't worry about it. It's probably for the better," she flashed a depressive smile as she rummaged through her purse, pulling the faux leather strings taught and tucked it high underneath her armpit. Char had no one here now. We all surrounded around her, but no one was on her team. They saw her as the enemy.

Char was good to me in a lot of ways when my dad was alive. I never could tell if it was because the way to my dad's heart was through me. I always held his heart, even if I didn't know it. Hollowed guilt ached in a radiant heat through my chest that wanted to scream out in steam like a tea kettle, but I held it all inside me and let it simmer me down to mush instead. Heavy steps clomped up the wooden stairwell to the main floor from the basement until an incredibly tall police officer ducked through the doorway and into the harsh dining room light that my dad loved for some reason.

"Who's the N.O.K.?" he talked at all of us, searching over our small group of family. "Forgive me," he looked down at his notepad. "Next of kin?"

"Uh, me," I was wildly unsure if I was who he was looking for because the officer looked at me several times and didn't say anything. "I'm his son."

"Alright, come over here please," he waved me over and pointed to Char with his worn-down pencil. "You too."

"Yes?" It felt like I was standing in front of the classroom, trying to solve a math problem. I was horrified and embarrassed. Nothing sounded better than to run into the woods and hide, bury myself under frozen ground and let the weight of the earth press down on me to drown out the pressure inside my ribcage. "Can you tell me what happened or what's going on?"

"Your father died around 12:03 a.m. Paramedics were called, and they tried reviving him for about thirty minutes until there was absolutely no way to bring him back. His body stiffened and skin turned blue. They utilized an AED four times but it wasn't successful. I'm sorry," his eyes softened when he looked down at me and shifted uneasily over to Char. "Can I get your name, son?" he asked.

"Vaughn-Shane Camarda."

"Age?"

"Twenty-two," I hesitated.

"Phone number?" he rounded off question after question. "Do you know if your father did drugs of any kind?"

"No, he didn't," Char was the first to lie. Every part of my body froze, feeling unsure of what I should actually say or what I should keep under covers. *Weed doesn't kill you, though. Does it?* I didn't really know anything about it other than it equalized my dad from his personality disorder. I couldn't help my gunshot reaction as I looked at Char lie so easily to the officer about Dad's habits that might've very well explained everything.

"Alright, well, they'll find out what actually killed him

when they get him to the morgue. You'll know soon enough. For the time being, you'll get death certificates with a pending status for cause of death. Then, you'll get corrected ones when they're done with the autopsy," he shoved his tattered green notebook into the left breast pocket of his uniform. "Would you like to go see the body before they take him out?"

Fuck.

I didn't know if I wanted the last incredibly bright moment we had together to be the last thing I remembered him by, or to have guilt eat me away when I couldn't see him anymore and didn't choose to see him one last time. I didn't have time to think it through, weigh the consequences of both actions, so I breathed in sharply and—

"I'm going to see him," Char blurted out as the cop folded his lips into his mouth and looked over at me, waiting for an answer.

"I'm going to," I said.

"Alright, we can have a couple of you at a time only since it is cramped in the basement. When you go down, he's partially in a bag, ready to depart. His clothes are still on him, but they won't come back with him. They'll be examined and incinerated," he faded into the background as no one listened to the maximum capacity rule and we all funneled down the basement stairwell to see him.

Millions of times, I'd come barreling down those steps into the cool basement to watch television. Dad and I had talks on those steps about life as he folded both our laundry because he hated how I didn't fold it just like him. When our family was together back then, as it is now in our house for the last time, he would play his electric guitar in the basement. His drawing table was down there, and the computer moved down there once

everyone moved out after the divorce. I spent hours in that basement playing Roller Coaster Tycoon and The Sims as I fended
off those disgusting brown centipedes from attacking me. Inside
that basement, I spelled out my first swear word and got smacked
hard from my mother before I finished the last letter. As a kid,
I had nightmares after watching the Leprechaun movies about
him living in the basement. Brian and Chelsey made me say my
first swear word in that basement, right by the scary furnace that
would explode into flames every time the igniter kicked in.

The body bag was grey. Not quite what I pictured in my
head, but I looked at his covered feet first, poking out at the top
like they would when I'd lay under blankets and look down at
my feet facing the ceiling. One black zipper stopped at his chest,
where I saw he wore his black bedtime tank-top with holes in it
from years of wear and tear. His long beard, which he was so
proud of, looked off color from the contrast of his blue-hued skin.
Dad's eyes were closed and his mouth slightly open, showing his
incredibly white teeth. We didn't establish turns, but I went first
without even thinking about it.

My legs felt numb, heart crept into my throat with the
thought of what his body would feel like after death—if it would
feel hard and cold or still warm and filled with life like I remembered. My thoughts, my feelings, and my actions were all on auto-
pilot. There was nothing I controlled in this room, not even what
I wanted to do next. I leaned over to the ground and kneeled next
to my father. My eyes were so transfixed on his mouth, looking for
any sign of life entering back into him, or to see his soul leave his
body—if it waited for me and hadn't left already. What made me
think souls even left out of the mouth? I tried conjuring powers I
never had, raising him from the dead with just my sight and pain.
I prayed to God and any other holy being out there that I could

think of.

Everything. I tried *everything*.

But magic wasn't real. God didn't feel real in this room other than the peace of holding my shit together so I wouldn't absolutely break down in front of everyone. I wasn't put on this earth with extraterrestrial powers that could shift time and bring a human back from the dead, no matter who they were. This was real. It was everything that I didn't write about in my stories and everything that I couldn't change with the easy press of a backspace. His cheek was cold against mine as I leaned in gently to hug him.

"I love you, Dad," I whispered into his ear while I held my breath for his reply. Against my own plan, I leaned in and kissed him on his cold cheek before I felt my visit expire. I had my closure, both ends of happily ever after and the chilled skin of a dead body. I stood back by the stairs while someone grabbed onto my shoulder and squeezed reassuringly.

Char took her turn. She took her turn for everyone when she melted down over my dad's dead body. She wailed and cursed life for such an unfair twist of fate, hands banging on the ground around him. There were no demons or ghosts that entered into her body and took her over, even though she acted possessed on the area rug Dad was laid for resuscitation. What the paramedics, coroner, officers, and my family watched was Char feeling primal instincts surge through every nerve ending in her body. Her ship sailed on without her, left her back on poor land. Her income died with him. While the reality of a life without my father settled in, Char's greatest nightmare shot through her body like someone lodged fireworks in her shattered soul.

I kept composure because whatever would come after this would be hard, but I would survive it. Char, on the other hand, witnessed the death of not only her lover but also her livelihood.

Chapter Twelve
PRICE TAG

Once they took his body away, I felt terrified. Nobody could touch anything in the house that he touched. At least, that's how it went inside my head. It didn't happen that way on the outside. I sat at the dining room table, staring at the edge of the table closest to the orange painted kitchen and vinyl flooring that had been there since Dad installed it when I was a baby. Everyone else moved around in blurry motions. Char. Well, she cried a lot more and told us how she just couldn't believe he was really gone and how sorry she was for me.

Char and I hugged a lot while Chelsey shot dirty looks over at me like I was hitting on her husband or something. It was well known my family didn't like Char nor trust her in any sense of the word. I didn't trust her myself, but it didn't get in the way of my compassion for her pain. There wasn't anything wrong with what she was saying or her actions. Just, I guess I wasn't the most understanding when it was my grief, too.

"Can we go downstairs for a minute?" I grabbed Char's hand and pulled her away from my family who debated in the kitchen about something I wasn't paying attention to at all.

"Yeah," she followed as we descended down the thinly carpeted stairwell, caked in dust around the edges where the vacuum couldn't reach. The body bag wasn't there anymore, but I swore I could see the lighter color of the bag on the floor where dirty clothes were pushed to the side in a circular pile like some type of grave marker. I turned around at the furnace and looked into her red, swollen eyes and the soft wrinkles around her face from smoking for all those years.

"What are you worried about?" I threw the question out there, into the rumbling white noise of the furnace running.

"You're going to kick me out. I know it. I don't have anywhere to go, I'm not ready. My friends tell me you're going to kick me out in the street with nothing. I don't know what I'm going to do or where I'm going to go. This is all I have. I don't have my own place or things. This is it! This is all I have," she wailed.

"I'm not kicking you out on the street," I tried talking over her rambling, but she wouldn't listen. "Honestly, that's not even anything to be worried about. I don't know why they would tell you—"

"If only this would've happened a couple months from now," Char sobbed harder into one of my dad's worn bandanas he used as a handkerchief.

"What?" I locked eyes with her as she crunched her nose into the bandana and blew. She was lucky that I was mostly numb to everything, that I had some type of control over my facial expressions and actions, otherwise, I would have snapped—exploded into a raging ball of energy.

"He kept saying how he was going to get life insurance in a few months," Char wiped her eyes with her sweatshirt sleeve. "It's just so sad this couldn't have happened in a few months instead of now, I mean. He was going to split it down the middle. It would have taken care of us both in the end," she stepped back from me, almost falling over onto the ground, but she caught herself on the stairwell.

All I can remember was the ringing in my ears as I looked at her cry, blow her nose, and keep mumbling about life insurance and a couple months down the road. I heard that money doesn't mean anything when someone you love dies, because there is no price tag on how you feel for someone. Some people can't be bought, and maybe money would make life suck less because you could focus on grieving instead of your everyday struggles, but my love and grief were so overpowering that all the money in the world wouldn't shift or erase any debilitating sadness away. It felt like someone crushed me over the head with a heavy object. The air stung my lungs and my vision blurred. I needed out. I needed out immediately.

"Yeah," no part of me agreed with her. The conversation simply needed to end. There weren't any words to say about how true her colors vibrated out into the fluorescent light of the basement—dark greens and blacks that I couldn't see but felt deep inside the gaping hole inside my soul that ached with every heartbeat. If one thing stuck with me after that sleepless night, after the war ended and the tears dried up, it was that.

If only this would've happened a couple months from now.

How about what if this never would have happened, Char? How about that...

"Everything okay?" mom handed me a cup of vanilla chamomile tea from the oak spice cabinet above the microwave. I bought it earlier that year for Dad.

"Yeah," I sipped the piping hot liquid and felt it painfully burn all the way down into my belly. It made me cough, and I had to put down my mug to choke it down. At least the burning was real. It let me know that physical pain existed still outside the nuclear winter inside my chest. "I'll talk to you about it later," I looked over at Char, holding onto the door as she used it to steady herself after walking up the stairs.

"Do you want any tea?" Mom asked her.

"No, thank you," she waved her away with a shaky hand and walked upstairs to Dad's bedroom.

There was no price tag that would make losing my father okay—no amount of money, no success, even if it meant I'd never publish a book in my entire life, I would choose him over any of it. I'd live poor on the streets or risk my own health to keep him alive because he would have done the same thing for me. There were no price tags in this story. Only one body tag I wish I never had to see.

Chapter Thirteen
EXTENDED FAMILY

I tried sleeping that night. I tried hard. Every part of my body ached, but I laid with my mom on the uncomfortable futon, in a pillow fort we made to try and make the stiffness somewhat comfortable. We napped in rounds. Not purposefully, only by accident. Part of me wished it would rain the next day. Isn't that what happens after someone close to you passes? The weather mourns with you? Pittsburgh is known for our long streams of grey days, so I guess I would take that for what it was.

The day after was a barrage of a million visitors. Family came and went, Mom left to get clothes for work and came back, Char left with my sister a couple of times because she needed a ride to the doctor's office and didn't want to be alone just yet. Me? I thought I wanted to be alone—until I was alone. I laid down on the pillow fort stacked in the corner of our black futon and forced myself to drift into unrested sleep. Every thirty minutes or so, I'd wake up thinking I was missing something, but the house was just an empty shell of a structure with the low rumble of air being pushed through the ducts from the furnace. Most moments, I was able to drift back into some type of sleep state. After a while, though, I just couldn't force myself back down into that darkness any longer and got up to shower.

Most of that day, I had my phone locked into my hand. It reminded me of when my Psychology of Death and Dying professor said that a friend of hers on Facebook shot their aunts entire funeral service live on her phone for all to see. Plans to cremate Dad didn't come till later, but I definitely posted about it briefly on my social media page. It wasn't because I wanted sympathy, though. Unless I did? I don't really know to be honest. My heart hurt harder than I'd ever felt before. I wanted the people that I cared about to know that and reach out, because it felt like I was drowning in my own body most of the time. Isn't that what social media is for anyways? To throw out our best or worst and hear what others say or feel about it—to get the approval or expose their disapproval in a, loosely termed, safe space?

Social media made me feel less alone in my grief. When I didn't want to eat, drink, sleep, or even sometimes breathe, I could flip through the outpouring of instantaneous love across the post I'd sent out about Dad. Truly, deeply, it wasn't about attention or pity. Although, I'd trick myself eventually and second guess my intentions when I felt especially vulnerable. I wanted it to be out there, more so because it felt relieving to write it into the abyss that is the internet. It could hang there on my page until my memories feed would show me it every year, until the day I died.

"How're you doing, sweetie?" Mom texted me.

"I'm okay. How's work?" I asked.

"It's alright. Can't wait to be out of here and with you. Are you doing okay? Need anything?" she asked.

"We need to go food shopping," I sent and slid my phone along the black kitchen counter next to the sink and dug through the barren pantry. There were noodles. Maybe I would be able to eat those. The emotional toll of losing Dad vanquished my appetite entirely. I forced myself to even drink coffee, and I had been drinking coffee since I was fourteen and realized then that I could go over twenty-four hours without sleeping. What a mess…

"We'll go once I get there. I should be done soon and then I'll come right over, okay?"

"Sounds good, Ma," I replied. "I love you."

"Love you so big, sweetheart," Mom disappeared from the chat once her lunch break ended.

Aunt Mar showed up a few times and talked loudly on the phone as she always had when things were going wrong. It wasn't much of a surprise to anyone when we found out that Little Angelo housed Dad's motorcycle and, when he was all about giving it up last night when he was here, he played hard to get when it came down to retrieving the bike. My aunt told me that it was important to have everything together all at once for when I had to close his estate. Whatever in the hell that meant.

"I swear if you don't give up my brother's bike!" she used some more colorful language than that, but this was the gist of what she meant. "That piece of trash, I'll kick his ass. Where is your sister?" she asked as she rummaged through the junk drawer in the kitchen.

"Chelsey is at the doctor with Char. Mom's at work, but she should be back soon," I mumbled from the futon.

"Alright. Are you going to be okay? I have some errands I need to run. Call me if you need anything, honey," Aunt Mar kissed me on the forehead before she went into the basement and left me alone again in the house.

"I'll be fine," I sighed, but she was already outside, headed to her truck.

"Hey," a message popped up in my notifications from Face-book Messenger. "You don't know me, but I saw about your dad passing and I wanted to tell you I'm sorry and here if you need anything." I didn't recognize his face, but I remembered seeing him in my newsfeed a few times in the past. We were newer friends on social media and I don't exactly remember who added who. Knowing me, I probably added him first.

"Thank you, that means a lot coming from a stranger," I replied.

"Oh, for sure!" he replied.

"It's been the hardest thing I've ever had to go through and deal with. It's kind of been the first couple moments I've had alone time. So many people have cycled through my house in the last day. It's exhausting."

"Want to talk about it?" he asked.

"Nah, I'm okay. Thank you, again," I replied back.

"I'm Trey, by the way. But you probably know that from Facebook lol."

I wasn't sure how he did it, but Trey made me smile in one of my darkest moments underneath a mountain of blankets and stale air that smelled like sleep. I wouldn't forget that.

"And I'm Vaughn, also obviously," I smiled at my phone as my neck cramped from the pillow.

"Nice to meet you," he replied. "Maybe we can get together soon or something? Get you out of your house, if you're interest-ed?"

"Very! Thanks again," I sent the message off in warp speed. "I'm going to try and sleep some, I think."

"Sleep well! I'm here if you need anything at all," I read the text, but my eyes drooped closed before I could reply. I didn't dream of Dad. I didn't dream of anything at all. It was black and heavy and drunken, but I hadn't drank any alcohol.

"Shit," Mom mumbled as she dropped her purse onto the kitchen floor.

"You're here," I spoke from the living room. "I need to shower."

"Sure, go ahead and shower. I'm going to powernap quickly before we go shopping, okay?" Mom changed into pajamas before creeping into the living room and onto the futon. I hugged her from the side and pulled myself off the comfy fort of blankets and pillows. From the carpet, to the vinyl flooring, to the walls, cabinets, chairs, and countertops, everything felt just as lifeless and cold as Dad's cheek had when I said my goodbyes. I walled up inside my body and pushed back the memories that haunted me everywhere I went inside this house. Not one inch of it wasn't tainted with the memory of Dad and there was nowhere to escape.

I forced the bathroom door closed, even though the wooden door was warped from years of steam, and leaned over the sink. Bloodshot eyes stared back at me in the mirror as I studied my face like I had any other morning, except this time felt different. Every feature I shared with Dad felt highlighted, wildly and painfully beautiful, but stuck out like sore thumbs that made the ache so much harder to bear. We had the same triangular nostril shapes and the same straight bridge that led up to the center of our eyebrows. Our head shapes were nearly identical, which helped me in the long run because I had the perfect shaped head for the bald cut. Dad and I shared hair genetics and lost our hair around eighteen and nineteen years of age. I was blessed with beautiful teeth; the upper teeth being what the family called "Camarda teeth" and the bottom I recognized to be a lot like my mom's. I recognized that I wasn't ugly by any means, but I hated everything that reminded me of Dad. Anything that we shared left a bitter taste of metal in my mouth that I couldn't shake.

"Ugh," I groaned and shut off the light to darken the bathroom so I could drown myself in the stillness. I cried in this bathroom more times than I can count, with the light off and a candle as I played Midnight by Coldplay. Baths were never my thing. A shower where I could sit cross-legged and let the scalding water smack against my head and body was the alternative for me when I wanted to think or cure the common heartbreak. But Dad's permanent absence wouldn't be cured by a simple shower, candlelight, and sad music. This was transformative and definitive. It changed me rapidly within a matter of seconds. I sat underneath the pelting water, without music or a candle to light the small bathroom, and plugged my ears with my index fingers so all I could hear and feel was the pelting water against my head.

The better part of my mom's thirty-minute nap was spent in the shower with my eyes and ears closed to erase myself for those quick fleeting moments. I wanted the water to erase who I was that night, the memory of it, and everything that I would become from it. I didn't want to die but I didn't want to exist either. It was a weird line, and I struggled with which side I wanted to end up on.

My phone ignited the steamed bathroom with bright white light and brought me out of my dazed shower thinking. I had a new message request from someone I'd never heard of before—wouldn't surprise me if it was someone who heard about my dad's passing and wanted to share their condolences and apologies with me. Fuck, am I over this.

"Hi Vaughn-Shane. I'm not sure if your dad told you about

me, but I am your sister. I'm our dad's daughter. I would like to talk to you someday… This is a very difficult time for all of us. Please call or text me sometime. Thank you."

"What the fuck?" My knees were already weak from the extended amount of heat I holed myself in, but this was too much, and I fell onto the bathmat, phone in my hand like it was a small injured animal. It couldn't be true. In that moment, I didn't want it to be true. I could barely handle what was already going on with everything and my own family, but the idea of an extended family I never knew about—years and years of secrets that were kept from me and those secrets surfacing now that he was gone and unreachable. This isn't happening.

"Are you alright, sweetie?" Mom knocked on the bathroom door. "Almost ready to go?"

"Yeah, sorry. Took my time in the shower. I'll be out in a minute," I choked down the swelling anxiety swallowing me whole inside the dark and steamy bathroom. Everything, all of it, was too much to handle. My brain fired off in a million sparks, triggering one after the other before it all became too much and I lurched over to the toilet to dry heave in silence so my mom wouldn't hear me suffering.

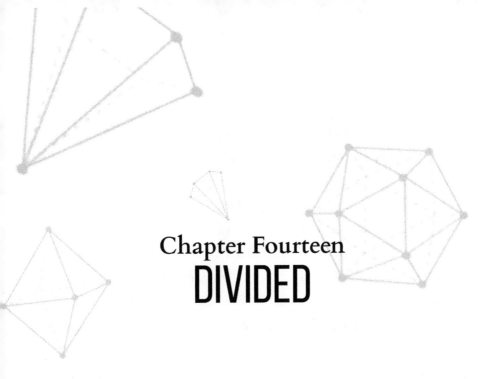

Chapter Fourteen
DIVIDED

My intention was not to tell anyone, but learning I had other siblings I never knew about was something that I couldn't keep in. Also, I learned very quickly that, as a whole, my family held the same secrets about these siblings of mine that I never knew about. I wasn't angry at them about it. Confused and hurt, yeah, because it was decided for me whether or not I would take it well, even though I was grown enough to make those kinds of decisions on my own. Knowing I had other siblings filled my heart to the brim in a time where there wasn't much that could do that. Yeah, my family was by my side every step of the way—all of my aunts, my uncle, Chelsey, Brian, and Mom—but the pressure of what to do next with this new information weighed heavier on my shoulders than I needed. Should I include them in the cele-bration of Dad's life or not? What about his possessions? Would I suddenly be kicked out of my house and these other siblings pushed inside because I was still the youngest of them all? I had no idea, and my bad habit of procrastinating important matters of business worsened when Dad died and I had all of this extra responsibility on my hands. This extended family of mine was pushed inside the little drawer in my head where I kept all of my problems locked up for when I was ready for them.

My family and I are known for doing everything last minute. Well, my mom, Chelsey, and Brian are known for that. We are procrastination queens and kings. Dad kind of operated that way, too. He planned a little bit better than us but, most times, he flew by the seat of his pants. That was our comfortable spot—figuring out how things would operate and making it work. It came in handy when I had to plan what we'd do for Dad's funeral service— if we even wanted a funeral service.

"Do you want a funeral, Dad?" I remembered asking him out of the blue years ago while I ran errands with him in his truck.

"Absolutely not. It's a waste of money and they're uncomfortable and stuffy. No funerals," he laughed and continued driving. *"Why'd you ask that?"*

"Just curious!" I laughed and looked out of the window into the sun with my sunglasses on.

"What do you want to do?" Aunt Mar asked as Sue, an old family friend of ours, sat in the dining room.

"No funerals. Dad hated them," I cleared my throat. "He doesn't want to be buried, either." My phone rang in the middle of our conversation from a number I didn't know. It had to be the coroner with the results of Dad's autopsy. "Hello?"

"Hi, may I speak to Mark Camarda, please?" the woman asked.

"Umm," I hesitated, "my dad's dead."

"Oh my goodness, I'm so sorry. I got the names mixed. Is this his son, Vaughn... Shane?" she asked.

"This is him. Who is this? What do you want?" I felt my

temper boiling over.

"This is Catherine, I'm a representative from Carnegie Mellon University and I'm actually calling in regards to your father who had passed. First of all, I'd like to extend my sincerest apologies about his passing and me reaching you so soon, but this is time sensitive and the phone call needed to be made."

"Okay? About what?" I cleared my throat and plopped down onto the couch.

"We reach out to the families of loved ones who have passed to ask, and no pressure when I ask you this, but if you wanted to donate your father's body to studies here at the college?"

"Excuse me?" I stood up and walked over to the window like this bitch was right outside my house talking to me. "No, I'm not interested at all."

"I understand this is a sensitive time, but we need to reach those families of persons who very recently passed because there is so little time to preserve the body for those studies after autopsy. Thank you for your consideration though, and again, I am terribly sorry for your loss."

"Bye," I hung up the phone and threw it across the room, cracking my phone case. "No, you can't study his *fucking corpse!*" I walked over to my phone and picked it up off the ground to inspect if it shattered. "Who even asks that? Days after he died! Days!"

"Yeah, no. They aren't going to get his body. You didn't say they could, did you?" Sue asked.

"No, they can't do that. They won't do that," Aunt Mar chimed in.

"Of course not! He's getting cremated and put in an urn or spread out somewhere or whatever. I don't know," I plopped down onto the couch and let my head fall into my hands.

"Don't worry about paying for the urn, I would like to get it for you," Sue offered.

"I couldn't let you do that, no," I protested.

"Come on, please? Let me do this for you," she begged as I looked over at my open laptop on the dining room table.

"Let her buy the urns if she wants to buy the urns, Vaughn," Aunt Mar backed her up and gave me no choice but to accept the offer. It didn't take long for me to choose which one I wanted for dad—a beautiful muted blue color, accented with silver around the lid, with carved silver birds taking flight in a curved pattern on the body. Dad loved birds and bird watching. He would do it for hours and hours in the summer days. As a gift, I bought him a *Birds of Pennsylvania* book and he would quote different bird names, rapid fire, after only a year of reading and spotting. It was incredible to me because Dad was never a reader. I mean, he read some really early versions of my young adult fiction book, *Cancel*, that were wildly hilarious and messy.

Sue ordered the amount of mini urns that matched the big urn that I would get to keep for the Celebration of Life I wanted to plan for him instead of the bells-and-whistles funeral production.

My brother and sister, her husband, and Mom were over at the house two days before the celebration. Chelsey had an amazing gift of keeping important photos and, well, almost everything you'd want to have for memories. Sometimes, to her dismay, she kept all the photos of our childhood and some of dad's childhood, too. Mom and Dad weren't ones to keep many photos, or at least keep them out of destruction. Chelsey, on the other hand, was a pro at preservation. While Brian and I planned to go prep the food the day, I took on the task of organizing the memorial board full of Dad's old photos.

I took the plastic grocery bag full of photos and scattered them along the beige carpet to pick the best ones. Mom and Chelsey fought over something that I mostly blocked out. Brian tried to calm the situation but that only fueled Chelsey's drunken rage-cloaked pain.

"Vaughn," she called out to me.

I ignored her on purpose because I knew what she was going to ask.

"Hello? Are you listening to me?" she yelled louder.

"What? Oh, I'm sorry. I wasn't paying attention. What's going on?" I asked from the floor of the dining room.

"Shot?" she asked and held up a shot glass, filled to the brim with brown liquor.

"No, Chelsey. I really shouldn't." I buried my face back into photos.

"Come on, bud. Don't be lame and come take a shot with me," her words slurred deeper as she started to cry.

"Fine, I'm coming," I got up and took the shot glass from her as she gripped the neck of the nearly-empty bottle and swigged right from the opening.

"Chelsey," David called out to her from outside.

"Coming," she left me with the shot still lingering and burning over every crevice inside my mouth.

Quickly, I leaned over the kitchen sink and spit it down the drain, rinsing my mouth out with water and spitting again. I set the glass in the bin of dirty dishes collecting in the sink in hopes that since there were no more shot glasses that the drinking would stop.

"How're the photos coming along, baby?" Mom pulled me in for a hug as Chelsey burst in from the back door.

"Fuck you, dude! *Fuck you!*" she screamed and pointed angrily at her husband and slammed the door. They both enjoyed the drink, more than they should, in my personal opinion. But I kept my head down because this was how she grieved. I had to be okay with the anger and screaming and crying because grieving was her right. Not everyone could shove it down and swallow the grief like I did.

"What in the hell is going on?" Mom made herself tea as Chelsey picked up the bottle again and Brian pulled open the door to go talk to David.

"Nothing, mother. Mind your own business," she yelled at her.

"Hey, little girl! I'm just trying to help you! I don't know why you're getting all pissy with me in the first place?" Here started World War 385 with those two...

"Don't fucking talk to me like that! Mind your own damn business. That's your problem! You're always in other people's business. You're just like your mother!" Chelsey screamed at her as Brian burst through the back door, face red from whatever conversation happened with David outside.

"What in the fuck is going on between you two? Seriously?" he threw himself on the front lines as they battled it out, like they always had for as long as I remember.

They all went at each other's throats while I sat and hummed to myself, holding in every terrible thing I could say about any of them at any moment. I held in the air, compressed it further in the combustible space in my chest that was already filled to the brim. They all went for the throats, though, and said all of the most extreme and worst things about each other inside the small space of the galley kitchen.

What would you do, Dad, if you were here right now?

He wouldn't let them keep fighting or sit here, weak, trying to ignore it, like I was. Dad wasn't weak like me. He was resilient and a survivor. He spoke out when things were unfair or wrong. Dad moved in when action was needed. He eased things when tensions were heightened and when emotions felt scattered and uncontrollable. He was the voice of reason.

Me, his son, was defected and let the war continue until someone, or all of them, would be further damaged and cry, curse at each other more, or become physical.

You are defected. You don't know what you're doing. You're a failure. Look at you, sitting there while you let your family fall apart. You are nothing like Dad.

I felt the snap inside my chest, the screaming of pressure release and explode out in a violent ringing inside my ears that wouldn't stop until it was all out.

"Shut the fuck up, all of you! I'm tired of hearing you fight about petty bullshit! This is *my* house and if you can't get along then get the fuck out of it! The door is right there! I'm tired of your constant fighting! It's been years of this bullshit and I'm tired of it!" I yelled louder than I ever thought I could in a rage that made me see nothing but white as I threw the bag of photos across the room. I got up off the ground and stomped into the kitchen as my sister saw herself out and yelled at David to drive her home. "There is no more *fucking* alcohol in Dad's—*my*—house until I say so! Do I make myself absolutely clear? I'm tired of all of this and all of you fighting! I have enough shit to deal with, and you guys aren't helping it get any easier for any of us!" I poured out every bottle of liquor in the house and threw them into the garbage bag so hard they shattered. "Bunch of fucking alcoholics, I swear!" I marched back to my pile of scattered photos and continued to pick the ones of Dad that brought me back from my blind rage.

The Sheraton Pittsburgh Hotel at Station Square, where I used to work as a front desk supervisor for a few years, and where I built an incredible support system during my time there, donated an entire banquet room for Dad's celebration of life. Hotel policies didn't allow outside food to be prepared and brought since it was a unionized hotel, but they bent the rules a little bit for me since I was one of their own and they wanted to help me as much as possible.

Almost all of my family was in attendance. Even family I hadn't really remembered from when I was a baby, but family who Dad sort of kept in contact with for the most part in recent years, were there. Against my gut instinct, John was in attendance, sitting at a table with one of my good friends, Angelina, her mother, and Angelina's boyfriend, who helped my brother with food setup.

John and Angelina sort of knew each other. There was a brief time in which I didn't talk to her much while I dated him, unfortunately, but we still stayed close friends after it ended and graciously reconciled as I had with Brandon. Out of the entire room, we had taken up at least three-quarters of the banquet space while another clan of Char's people occupied the last quarter of the room, staring over at us all with dark, judgmental eyes. If looks could kill, I would have been dead a million times over.

"Vaughn-Shane," my grandmother called me over to where she stood in front of Dad's memorial table with the poster board, urn, and giant flowers that had been sent from a family friend in Florida.

"Yeah?" I leaned into her as she continued to wave me closer so she could whisper without being heard.

"This is Frankie," she nodded to a bigger gentleman standing beside her with his back to Char's table and all her family and friends, Little Angelo included, whom I didn't really want there or thought should be there. "You remember him, don't you?"

"No. No, I don't," I spoke directly.

"I didn't think you would," she rubbed her hands on her pants and swallowed. "Listen to Frankie, okay?"

"Son," he put his hand down hard on my shoulder and leaned in all too close for comfort. "What I need you to do is kick her out of her house, do you understand me? She cannot stay one more day in that house or it'll become harder to get her out later."

"What?" I asked.

"Listen to me. You're not listening to me at all. She needs to be kicked out of the house tonight. If you have any trouble at all, call the police and explain the situation. Do you hear and understand the words that are coming out of my mouth?" his mustache and beard were wet from when he licked his lips and continued talking. I already knew she was going to be kicked out. It was just a matter of when and how soon that I was figuring it out.

"S—sure. Yeah, I will tonight," I agreed in a desperate attempt to end the conversation.

"They are bad people, that bunch, and they don't need to be in that house any longer than you've already allowed. Do not brush away my warning, son. Are you listening? Do you understand me?" his voice felt like it echoed in my ribcage as his hand pushed down harder on my shoulder.

"Yep," I flattened my lips into an uneasy smile and escaped from underneath his pressed hand. "I forgot something, I'll be right back."

"I'm truly sorry for your loss. He was a great man," Frankie tapped hard against my shoulder again and let me escape the incredibly awkward and uncomfortable conversation right in front of Dad's memorial table.

I was getting tired of this, being told what to do and when to do it. Given awkward, loose ended warnings about who I should stay away from and who I shouldn't. It plunged me further into my inescapable anxiety, so deep that I was numb to everything and anything. I was beyond the threshold of hysterics and anger and sadness. Anxious, psychotic laughter boiled inside my belly and begged to come out and poison my mind, but I didn't even have time to succumb to the warning signs my body screamed out at me that blurred into one constant buzzing white noise that I adapted to as my new normalcy.

Chapter Fifteen
ENTER VILLAIN

An elixir killed my dad.

Cocaine, alcohol, and fentanyl.

Accidental, the coroner ruled.

You brought it into our home. You coated the walls, the

floors, and the furniture in gasoline and lit the match when you brought those into our home. You started Dad's clock the day you met him, at your run-down bar where you worked under the table. When you would sit in our living room, after I'd come home from work, you'd nod off over and over again, and Dad would yell at you to wake up and stop nodding off like that.

"I'm just tired," you'd retort with that weird clicking thing you did with the tip of your tongue when you were disgusted at something.

"Then go to bed! Don't go nodding off on the couch like you're doing. You look ridiculous!" Dad would badger you and you'd sit there, quietly in acceptance or shame. I couldn't tell the difference. There was a time that I felt bad for you, Char. When you realized what Dad was capable of—the degrading things he could say because of his mental illness, but always out of love. It was a different, bittersweet kind of mental illness he carried and pushed onto his loved ones, but only because he cared too much. I was the one who understood where you were with him most. Before you were ever in his life, before you started counting down his days, testing the waters and playing chicken with death, I knew him.

"You're such a jerk," you'd laugh when you'd say it because you wanted to voice your opinion but not set him off on one of his screaming tangents. It was a risky game that you played horribly. Some days, I couldn't tell if he actually liked you at all. Let me go back to what I said about feeling bad for you, though. It wasn't a pitiful emotion. It was genuine. We understood Dad in a lot of personal ways others would have never been able to grasp unless they witnessed it first-hand. You had to do the dishes a certain way, fold the towels how he folded them, and sweep all of the carpets before he came home from being away at work. Truthfully, it was a small price to pay to live here for next to free. It was kind of funny, thinking on it now; I was the only other person in that house to pay a bill. Dad took care of the both of us full-time. I paid the cable bill. It was never too extensive or out of reason. Dad did a lot of shit for us at that house. I don't think you realized it until he was gone for good, until it was just us two in that house.

We both knew your time was ticking, too. Not for your death, because why would the person who gave it to him in the first place be the one to go instead? You and I both knew this wasn't a book or movie. What was fair didn't happen for things like this. Your time ticked down until the day your stay in Dad's house expired. There were a few landmarks you had to hit first on your grand exit.

The week after he died, I froze his bank accounts. You had already snuck in and taken everything for yourself because, at the end of it all, you wouldn't see a dime out of his estate. His bank account was your payout for your grief—a little something to soften the blow of losing the one you "loved." I knew the exact spot you drained his account in two transactions, both with cameras in view of the ATM you used. His bank had all the evidence in the world against you at my disposal. Regardless of what I did with the evidence, they refunded the money into the account and closed it out properly. I didn't put in the energy to press charges against you because it was energy I couldn't afford. I was walking a very thin tightrope, holding onto what was left of my sanity. I had to keep the house in order. I had to pay the bills because you surely weren't putting forth any effort. *Strike one for you, Char.*

We had our battles after he died. You couldn't be trusted once he was gone and after I found out you had drained his bank account. It was kind of Noah to install a security system in the house that you were too daft to ever notice. Instead of battling you to leave the house, I let you stay in the house and watched from my desk at work. I did this for two weeks, and you broke the rules I'd clearly laid out to you:

1.   No one other than you is allowed in the house.
2.   Do not ever leave the house unlocked. If you leave the house, you lock the house and wait till I get home because you hadn't earned a key after my uncle helped change all of the locks.

There were only two rules and you broke both. You allowed Little Angelo in the house once while I was away at work. He didn't do anything that extensive, only stood in the kitchen by the microwave in perfect view of my hidden camera. You were rummaging through the basement in Dad's desk for something. I never found out what because I never confronted you about it. Knowing that you had already drained his bank account, I could only guess that it was for anything that could be sold and wouldn't be noticed by me. Unlucky for you, I went into hyperdrive, remembering every single little detail about how I left the house, so that even if you dropped a toothpick behind the couch, I'd notice.

I watched you get ready for the day or run to the gas station or wherever. I think you said to grab a bite to eat, but you were drugged when you came home. I could see that from the camera. *Strike two.*

"I asked you to not leave the house unlocked, Char. It's not that hard, and I only gave you two rules and urged you to not break them, and you told me you wouldn't." I texted you as you sat on my couch. Three employees walked up to me in succession and asked me a question that I totally blew off and ignored in my rage of anxiety. They understood, though, and I apologized to them later about it, but that's not the point. I was playing big brother, babysitting you and watching you like a hawk on the camera, listening to your conversations about what you were doing and where you were going. I listened to you sob over the phone about how much you missed him and that you *just couldn't believe* he was gone. If I had to hear you say that one more time as you disrespected my simple instructions, I was going to lose my shit.

"I'm not going to just sit outside until you're done working, Vaughn. Give me a key and the doors won't stay unlocked when I leave."

"You will never have a key to my house. If you leave, you stay out until I get home."

"You can't just kick me out of the house. I live here, too, you know!" you replied to my rapid-fire rage texts that I'd never say to your face because I was too much of a coward.

"No parts of Dad's house is your house, do you understand me? If you want to stay there, then you have to follow the rules. It's easy as that!" I breathed heavy when wildfire heat pulsated at the surface level of my skin. Adrenaline shot through my fingertips and sparked at every nerve. I blinked about a thousand times as my eyes shot around the blank computer screen, ready to meltdown and explode into an uncontrollable anxious rage. I felt out of control of everything that happened. *I was* out of control of everything that happened.

"He's making me stay in this house because he won't give me a key, sis. I don't know what to do," she cried in the phone to her sister who was on speaker phone. I caused her pain and it broke my rage instantly. I made her cry. *Me.*

Dad would be ashamed of you. He told her you'd never make her leave the house—you'd never kick her out and let her live there forever. That was what he wanted and you're destroying all of it. You're pathetic. You aren't a good person, Vaughn. You are weak. You are the villain, here, not her. Char might have brought the cocaine into the house that killed him, but you are setting fire to everything after him. Cocaine killed him, but you are murdering his legacy.

My fingers pressed deep into my eyes. I wanted to throw up; to get the guilt out of my body so I could feel empty and numb like I did before instead of feeling like I was drowning in rage, pain, and worry with no safety preserve or energy field to beam me up. That's when I heard it—your final words that showed me the edge.

"That son of a bitch can't kick me out of this house. Him and his pathetic family are all assholes. Fuck them. They all can go fuck themselves, useless pieces of nothing!" Char screamed into the phone at her sister as she sat on the futon couch we've had since Mom and Dad bought it for my sixteenth birthday. She huddled over a small pink, circular mirror I've watched her put her eyeliner on in for years, crush up more of the real villain in this story, and snort. I watched her sit in my office chair and snort one, two, and three lines in succession. Char teetered on the couch as she slouched further and further between her legs. *Strike three.*

"You're gone," I wrote. "You think for one fucking minute I'd let you stay in my house after all you've done? You have zero respect for me or Dad's house! You don't listen to my simple rules, you bring people into my home without my permission," my fingers smashed against the screen faster than I'd ever typed before. "You can bad mouth me all you want. I really don't care what you think about me," I didn't really like myself to begin with. "But you will not bad mouth my family while I let you, out of my own kindness, stay here for free. Let alone do drugs in my living room? Are you serious? After what killed dad, you're going to do drugs in my living room?"

"Vaughn, I'm not doing any drugs. What are you talking about? I'm not talking bad about your family at all?" she responded.

"Char, I have a camera hidden in the house that records everything. I watched you with my own eyes and heard you. You leave tomorrow."

It was the soundest decision I'd made since Dad died. It was the most emotionally driven decision, but the most powerful I'd felt through all of the self-hatred and grief I'd succumbed to. I could've mentioned the bank situation, too. How she took his bank card before the police came and tried resuscitating him, and how she lied about it all night when I asked, repetitively, where it was. I let that rest, though, because it wasn't my place or right to punish her.

There were a lot of people I could hate in this world. A lot of people I was wronged by and a lot of people who wore me down to the thin metal below like a destroyed pencil eraser, but hate never found a home in my heart. There was no code or understanding for hate within my body. My parents raised me without a single hatred-born bone in their body. I found that hate and hatred for other people was learned and accepted over time. For it to survive and thrive, we first needed to allow it into our bodies. I wasn't going to let that in.

Char gave me every reason to hate her, but my heart hurt for her more. I cried for her during nights alone in my bedroom. Her wailing sob cut through me because I felt her unfiltered pain. I felt her loss throughout every inch of my body. I lived her pain and desire for numbness. I spent countless days fighting with the real villain about how I treated her in the end and what would happen to her after I edged her out of my life and home. Some nights, I'd lay awake thinking about her and what she was doing and how she'd survive. I'd worry for her and about her. It was never a desire to welcome her back into my life because the time where our lives intersected expired when we lost the person we loved more than anything in this world. The villain in my story was never Char, nor was she the villain in my dad's story. Char, like every single person in this world, was simply human. That's all we ever were and ever will be.

Chapter Sixteen
2017

My family made a pact that every New Year's, we'd travel together to different places. As our introductory to this new tradition of ours, Brian kicked it off with a mild allergic reaction to the shellfish that snuck into his dish at a hotel restaurant in Erie.

Mom and her boyfriend were late arriving since they hit a storm on their way up, and she had to work before the drive as well. Thankfully, they made it, but well after our incredibly mediocre seafood dinner. Probably should've played it safe with a pizza.

"Let's get this party going, kids," Chelsey lifted her cup, filled to the brim with liquor and a little bit of mixer. Silently, I sighed and lifted my cup as our family began the end of one horrific year. "Who wants to go drink in the pool?" She took off her pants and showed she already had her swimsuit on.

"Jeeze!" I laughed and covered my eyes.

"Oh, shut up, it's a swimsuit, you weirdo," she punched my arm and made me fall onto the spare chair.

"This is a nice hotel, bud. How'd you pick it?" Mom asked.

"Oh, you know," I shrugged, "just some searching through photos on their website. My old boss recommended it to me." Sorry, I lied, Mom. To impress a guy I'd briefly dated, I used my employee discount for a room at the Sheraton Erie Bayfront Hotel. Needless to say, it worked and impressed him. His mom thought I was a creep, but she grew to like me a lot once I met her. I possess a certain kind of mysticism when it comes to getting other people's parents to like me.

"This is great," Mom's boyfriend chimed in as he walked out of the bathroom.

"Glad you guys like it. Want to go swimming?" I asked.

"We forgot our suits," Mom did her signature sigh within a disappointed laugh.

"I told you to remember them!" I laughed with her, even though Mom wanted to swim with her kids. Although more frequent now than a month ago, it was rare occasion that all three of her kids were together with her in one room, let alone on a trip together.

"I know, I know. Go have fun. We're going to hang out up here or maybe explore the hotel a bit," she hugged me before we all funneled out of Chelsey and David's room. "It's so nice to have all my babies in one room."

"Yeah, yeah," Chelsey joked with her.

Down in the pool, Brian tried to end his thirst streak by seducing two girls that were in the pool with us. He played EDM music from this little speaker he got for Christmas from Noah and blasted it until the batteries croaked.

"Oh, come on. What do you two lovely women have planned for the evening?"

"Oh, you know," the one farthest away from us replied.

"Alright, alright. I understand. I won't push any further," he laughed before he grabbed my foot and dunked me underwater. We wrestled as Chelsey jumped in and joined our little playful battle. The pool room was hot, the music blasted, and it had been a whole month since I drank any liquor, so my mixed drink hit me hard and fast. Sadness didn't creep its way into this New Year's Eve, my numbness didn't increase, and I had no struggle having a good time and letting loose with my siblings, whom I never spent this much time with. We grew up very much apart and independent from each other. Brian and Chelsey were always closer, and I sometimes envied that. In the bigger picture of our dysfunctional relationships with each other, I appreciated my distance. They didn't understand my choice to be guarded and walled up from everyone, including even from Mom. That was before. Even now, I knew this togetherness was fleeting and we would go back to our norms once the storm passed.

Mom and I grew closer after Dad died, but isn't that stereotypical? It was my last parent left alive on this world—one person of two who birthed me and cared for me through my entire life until this point. Of course, I'd become closer with her. I consider myself blessed that I have the opportunity to have her in my life more, and I seek that closeness with her.

"Ball's going to drop soon!" Mom yelled from inside the pool door.

"Let's roll," Brian dunked me underwater as I laughed and sucked in so much chlorinated water it nearly choked me.

"You—ass," I punched him in the arm before he helped me out of the water. Chelsey and I pushed him into the pool as he tried to get out himself, and he dramatically flopped around in the water. That was Brian, though. Always being the goofy one of the family.

"Y'all play too much," he pulled himself out of the water as Chelsey and I laughed and dried ourselves off. "See you ladies later! Pool party after the ball drops!"

"Yeah, your balls," I said loud enough so the two ladies could hear and elbowed him lightly.

"Not funny, bro. Not funny," he clenched his jaw tight. "Just wait till you fall asleep. I'm going to get you back and you're going to hate every minute of it."

"Whatever you say!" I ran for the elevator as the blast of cold froze me down to my core. There was some type of wedding going on at the hotel. People were dressed in suits and gowns as they looked in disgust at our small, soaked family, covered in tiny pool towels that reeked of chlorine and hard water. We took the elevator to the second floor and mad-dashed to get changed in time for the ball to drop.

We crammed into Chelsey and David's room, where all the snacks and liquor was stocked, and turned on the television. Mariah Carey performed. It was a loose definition of *performed* because half the time she stopped singing and tried to get the crowd to sing.

"Do we have Dad?" I asked, looking around the room for the miniature urn we brought of him to the hotel.

"Right here," Chelsey brought it out and set him on the table. "Shots?" she asked.

"Sure," Brian poured everyone a shot as we watched the time tick down in the last minute of 2016. Each number counted down in some abstract animation as celebrities and random Time Square-goers hugged and cheered, all with their eyes to the sky, up at the scintillate ball lowering down to the end of it all. We didn't cheer at all. We didn't yell or raise our hands in praise to the end of another fantastic, fulfilled year. We sat there in silence, in the hotel room with nautical décor, blue walls, and a beautiful darkened view of Lake Erie outside the window. My family dragged each other across the finish line like we were coming out of a warzone, broken, damaged, but not defeated.

With thirty seconds to go, I tried to hold onto every last one, remember each number that passed and the way the room felt muggy and the liquor warm in my hand through the small shot glass. I desperately tried to remember how many chip crumbs laid on the desk in my sister's hotel room, how everyone sat and what they wore, and how they stared at the television in silence—all of the stupid little things that no one pays attention to mattered to me in that moment. The way Chelsey held onto her husband when the clock chimed down with fifteen seconds to go. How Brian and I sat away from each other, alone in this crowded room. How Mom and her boyfriend sat together in the spare chair, her on top of him. The way the window felt cold against my back as I watched the time slip away with the last year Dad was alive.

There would be no moment in 2017 that he was alive for— he would never see my first book get published, or watch me thrive at my job or get another promotion, or do any more work for the community, or see me continue on, broken but more resilient than ever before. 2016 was ending, but so was their battle. The war of my world continued on with me at the forefront—a one-man army seeing everyone that I loved that cheered me on from the sidelines start to leave at the end of this game because their team was losing. I was losing.

Five seconds. I felt panic ignite inside my body, like it would before getting my blood taken or a shot at the doctors, but a million times worse.

Four seconds. My anxiety increased and multiplied by a million and one, like how it felt when going up the long, chained hill of the scariest rollercoaster.

Three seconds. Heat surged into my head and almost blinded me as I swallowed and felt the heat pulse behind my eyeballs and in my heartbeat.

Two seconds. I looked away from the television at the movement I caught out of the corner of my eye—my family prepping the shot Brian poured for us in the New Year. I followed their lead and moved the glass rim to my lips where the warm, brown liquor coated them and burned the tip of my tongue.

One second left.

I tipped my head back, took the shot as the television roared to life, lights flashed and danced as confetti covered everyone in Times Square. The ball ignited in a blinding light that I imagined could be seen forever as we all entered into 2017 with some type of metaphysical clean slate. The shot burned all the way down and drug me deeper into my numbed state that remained static at the surface. Every sound in the room went with it as a buzzing rang in my ears, like someone shot a gun right next to me.

"Happy New Year," I looked down at the text that lit up my phone, resting on my knee. I replied quickly to Trey as Chelsey went around and started to fill the shot glasses back up. She tried to fill mine but I put my hand over it.

"Oh, come on, we're celebrating!" she whined a little.

"I'm fine, Chels, honestly. I'll get another in a moment. That last one is still working its way through my body," I laughed.

"Alright, fine. Butthead," she did another for me as everyone took another shot. I could feel my mom watching me from her seat for my reaction to the new year. I've gotten better at hiding what I feel in my face. The numbness at least helped with something.

"You okay, baby?" she finally asked.

"Yeah," I hesitated and brushed her concern off. "Just texting!" I forced a smile as I buried myself back into my phone.

"I love you," she picked herself off her boyfriend's lap and walked over to hug me. I embraced her from the side as I stopped my uninteresting skim through social media.

"To Dad," Brian raised his glass as the words caught in his throat.

"To Dad," Chelsey joined in and tears flooded her eyes before they started freely pouring. They tried hard to hold it back, but the alcohol inhibited their strength and weakened their barriers. I knew they would cry tonight. They were the only ones who struggled to keep their emotions under control. Numbness wasn't a free-flowing option, so they thought drinking would help. I don't say I blame them, but they knew how I felt about their drinking and what it caused the last time we all drank together.

I grabbed onto Dad's urn and held it in my hand as they surrounded me for a photo of our hands wrapped around the small steel blue urn with a singular bird on the front. We staged our hands so I was holding it, while their hands wrapped around mine in an impossible interlock we'd never be able to recreate. Our shared tattoos showed in the photo, which was Mom's idea, and she took the photo. Once we were done with our impromptu photoshoot, we hugged, and Mom took more photos of my siblings and me embracing.

"I don't get it," Chelsey tried to hold back her sobs.

"What?" I asked.

"You never get emotional at all. You don't cry or show anything. All you do is sit there and I don't understand it."

"I don't know," I didn't want to be trapped in this room anymore. I wanted to be alone in my room, away from their emotional states teetering in and out of control. This wasn't what I wanted as my first memory of the new year, but this was what I would remember, regardless of what I wanted. As much as I had no say in how they conducted themselves and their emotional states and feelings, I had as much say in how life panned out. It wasn't fair to be stuck inside this small space and interrogated for how I conducted my feelings or my body when in elongated distress, but they voiced their opinions regardless. They weren't me, and I wasn't them, and that offended my siblings within their insurmountable grief.

For my entire life, I wasn't who they were. Thinking back on it now, I think what offended them most was not how I handled my grief, although they had issues with it, but how I didn't need them as much as they needed me. I've never considered myself above them. I never would. But as much as they struggled to swallow the unchangeable fact that Dad was gone, they struggled just as hard with the fact that I never needed them. I never needed anyone from my family. That's not to say I didn't want them in my life, though. It wasn't about desire. It was always about need, and my family grew up in tragically separated times, so we adjusted to that. We were functionally dysfunctional, and when they needed me most for their grief, I pushed them up and out of my walls. I temporarily erased the night we lost Dad.

It was a new year—hopefully a *better* year. Nothing about who I kept outside of my walls changed, even though I deconstructed from the inside out and chipped away piece by piece under the pressure of a thousand suns. I might've kept them out of my walls, but that didn't hide anything of what happened on the inside. My walls were glass and all eyes were on me.

Chapter Seventeen
THE MASSES

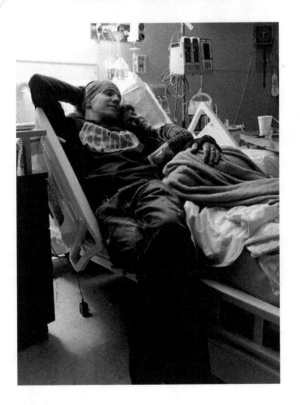

It was easy to block out Mom's cancer before Dad died. She dropped the bomb on me right before he passed, and how she had a doctor's appointment in January before surgery to remove it from the upper left lobe of her lung. Everything that happened after the news dropped made it easy to cover it with a sheet and push it aside. I didn't need to deal with it right then because crisis happened. It lurked in the background, waiting to sneak up and remind me that life was fragile and nothing guaranteed.

I remembered reading articles in my Psychology of Death and Dying course where both parents died in a tragic car accident and one child was left, barely holding onto life. My heart broke for the little girl, whoever she was, because she not only had to fight for her life, but once she pulled through, if she pulled through, there would be an even larger death she would have to accept to survive.

"I count myself lucky and blessed that I haven't lost someone close to me. I couldn't imagine what it would feel like," I remember speaking out in class after we watched the video clip of the accident. That was one day before Dad died. Now, my mom could be next.

A month and a half later, I was still shoving my foot in my mouth for what I said as I sat in the waiting room with my grandparents and my mom's boyfriend for her to go into surgery at Mercy Hospital. They assigned her a number that was projected onto a screen with another long set of numbers, all of whom were waiting to go under the knife, were under the knife, or were in post-op after they fixed whatever they needed to. My eyes ached from the strain when I fixed on the screen and zoned out. Little specks twinkled in my vision while others like me waited impatiently to hear about their loved ones. Everything smelled like old coffee and hand sanitizer and the hospital always had an uncomfortable chill in the air. It helped because I couldn't stop sweating.

"What's new with you, Vaughn-Shane? Anything?" my grandma leaned over and put her hand on my knee.

"Oh, you know. Just a lot of work and such. Dealing with

some of Dad's things still and writing," I sighed within a worn smile.

"You know, I'm really sorry to hear about your dad," she frowned. "That's terrible."

I could tell she was sincere, but my father's parents and my mom's parents never got along. They didn't really like him that much, which is another story for another day, but my grandma was incredibly sincere in her apology, and I read that clear as day on her face. I remember going to their house as a kid, and how I'd be looked at in a certain way that made me feel like an alien. It was never their intention and they were kind and generous people, always, but I knew that the pot was stirred and tipped over in the background. I was too aware for as young as I was back then. It's the same reason why I didn't want to watch little kid shows at that age because it all made me feel belittled and demeaned.

"Yeah, it's hard. Probably the hardest thing I've had to go through—still going through," I corrected myself.

"Oh, absolutely," she crossed her arms and looked forward at the nurse's desk. "And your writing? What's going on with your book? What was the title again?" she asked.

"Cancel! It's still a work in progress. Never ending," I laughed, although it kind of stung for me to admit it still wasn't an actual physical thing. I was embarrassed to be jammed in this state of almost with my book. My delayed successes aside, I hoped to God she didn't ask about school.

"Good, good. And school?"

Ugh.

"Once Dad died, I had to take a break for this semester. There's too much going on in my life to fully focus on school," my gaze fell down to my red and grey running shoes. I bought them cheap from Payless. "Like setting up his estate, and getting back to some kind of normalcy, and mom having this surgery," I stretched up high for no reason. I wasn't stiff in this uncomfortable hospital waiting room chair or anything. I just needed to do something with my body to fill the gap and distance myself from conversation.

"Well, when you get settled back in make sure you pursue college again. You're a smart man. You're going to do great things," Grandma's lip quivered like it always did, and Pap nodded his head when I thought he was totally zoned out of the conversation. Their rapid-fire interest and kindness didn't surprise me because it was infrequent, I just hadn't expect it here in this dark and stale waiting room. My heart swelled and I quickly had to patch the holes so I didn't lose it. This waiting room was no place to start crying because of kindness. There wasn't time to let my feelings rush in. I needed to be strong because... well, because I had to.

"Thanks, Gram," I smiled and sipped the cold coffee, swirling it around my cup with a thin white layer on the top where the cream had separated from the acidic liquid below. It was free, so I couldn't complain too much. I didn't even know why I was drinking more coffee in the first place when I had Starbucks on my way here. I needed something to occupy my hands and distract me; something I could use to drown my mouth so I didn't have to speak or feel the necessity of conversation anxiously tingle on my lips.

"They moved her to the operating room. Her status changed on the television," Mom's boyfriend's thick southern accent filled the crowded waiting room. Strangers flashed worried looks to check on their loved ones' status, too, to see if it changed. I couldn't help but to think about why they were there and what they had at stake. Was it life or death for them? Or was it just another procedure?

While we waited, I thought of the most recent memory I had of Mom that popped into my head first. When she came home and I showered before we went to the grocery store—it was a nice first trip out of the house and we had gotten a lot of our favorite snacks and some things for breakfast, lunch, and for dinner. Mom strained to turn on the light when we arrived back home from the store and dropped the bags onto the floor, her cellphone pressed against her shoulder to her ear as she talked to her boyfriend.

"Want to listen to a song that reminds me of Dad?" I asked.

"Yeah," Mom smiled at me as she brushed my cheek before heading into the bathroom. "Yeah, honey, let me call you back. I just got home from the grocery store and I'm going to help put them away, okay? Alright, love you, too, bye," she hung up the phone, finished in the bathroom, and walked back into the kitchen as I started playing *Where Are You Going?* by Dave Matthews Band.

The song hit me harder than I thought it was going to. I thought I could handle playing something that really struck the most chords when I thought of Dad. I wasn't ready even though I held it together. That's when I pulled out the black cherry ice cream that we bought at Kuhn's Market. It was cheap ice cream made by Golden, but it was his favorite. I ripped the protective seal open, lifted the lid as my mouth salivated, waiting for the first bite, and as the guitar strummed in the background and Dave Matthews sang the chorus, my spoon dug into the perfectly flattened layer. I lost it. I lost it all right there in my kitchen.

I cried and cried into the tub of untouched ice cream, nausea stampeded around my stomach like a march of protest, and the quick-fix patchwork I'd slapped on my walls trickled down into watery cement. Mom swooped in, shut off the music, and held me in the kitchen as I cried for the first time since driving home the night he died.

Mom attended every musical I had ever been in, every play, and every choir and band concert throughout high school. She was there for every triumph and haphazard failure. Whatever it was, she didn't care and wanted to support her little boy.

There was one point in time when I wanted to be an actor and knew I was destined to be famous on the Disney Channel. I had gotten picked up at this free ProScout event in Boardman, Ohio, and invited to the bigger event in Cleveland that cost a boatload of money we didn't have. It was one of those huge convention schemes where they promised you fame and fortune and an audience in front of top industry leaders across Hollywood and New York City.

There was a large hiccup once we got there. Mom and I didn't really know how hotels worked, and we hadn't paid for the room in advance and got screwed once we arrived because there was no money for the room. We both panicked, having spent all our money on the convention tickets, photos, and extra workshops that they'd offered to guarantee me a spot in the big leagues of Hollywood. Luckily, Pap saved the day and lent us money to stay there the night so we could go through the entire conference worry-free.

I protested her watching me while I paraded around the stage, looking absolutely ridiculous in my shoulder-length and highlighted hair. At the end of the day, after making it all the way to the end of the auditions and more parading around on this weird stage in a huge banquet space, I wasn't called to make it out to Hollywood. I was crushed. Mom, too, which made for an incredibly long and quiet drive home from Cleveland, broke, exhausted, and eyes a little more open to the grand scheme of conventions like that.

"I'm so sorry, sweetie. I know you're hurting and disappointed. I think you were amazing, and I can't understand why they didn't pick you, but you're still going to do great things one day," she ran her hand through my hair as she drove the three hours it took to get to Pittsburgh in a torrential downpour. I didn't want to hear her cheer me up. I wanted to be like the rain and drown in my sorrowful pity for myself. I was a big waste of time and money. I felt that, all of it, as I sat there with one headphone in one year, blasting Imogen Heap's Hide & Seek, and the other ear exposed to hear Mom.

Ever since I can remember, I've always had this sense of urgency to make myself feel worse to feel any better. If I was sad, I'd listen to sad music so I could wallow in my angst, and a sort of pressure I could never explain would build inside my chest, like I was a teapot waiting to scream. My methods were not healthy in any sense, and I found that I'd carried those bad habits with me into adulthood, through relationships, and my failures. It was my trick, my vice, and how I'd make the pain go away; keep drowning yourself because eventually you'll stop breathing and it will win till it gets tired or bored of making you hurt. While I suffered in the quiet pounding of rain against her silver Chevy Cobalt, Mom was there for all of it.

I was there for all of it.

When she made it out of procedure, we were herded down dark hallways in the late hours of the hospital. They made exceptions for visitors of patients in procedure or post-op because every minute could be someone's last, whether they were getting stitched up from a deep cut or they broke a bone or they were getting the left lobe of their lung extracted from their body. Nothing was ever guaranteed.

One by one, we filed down the section of the hospital where they kept her—dark salmon highlighted the walls and floor with equally dark blue floor tiles. Curtains were the only thing to separate the rooms from other post-op patients, which felt wrong, but I guess they knew more about what they were doing than I ever would. I brought up the rear of our small group since they only allowed a few to visit at a time, so it wasn't sensory overload for Mom when she finally saw us again after surgery. I was holding back anyways because I didn't know what she'd look like, how I'd act, or what would change about me once I saw her in those ugly white paper gowns and the hospital socks she loved so much. Mom loved those socks so much that we went on a late excursion on a school night, years ago, to Walmart so she could find herself a pair of those hospital socks with the "grippies on the bottom," as she called them.

"This is Walmart," the employee replied and pointed over to the sock section, which could mean one of two things: they either had them or they were judging my mom for her hopefulness. Needless to say, it was the latter.

Stretched out on her bed under thin hospital blankets, Mom had wires attached to her in all places, and some type of breathing apparatus that dangled in front of her mouth with two prongs lodged into her nose sat loosely on her face. Steady beeps cycled through their monotonous song as she gazed over everyone there to see her—parents, boyfriend, and me. Her boyfriend briefly went in to hug her first, Pap and Gram went next, as I leaned in last to hug her as tight as I thought acceptable. Within seconds, I pulled away and felt the cold, dead hand around my neck tighten its grip over my esophagus. *Run. Run away and come back when you're done.* I walked over to the window and stared out it like I could see something exciting from it. The others talked over each other, ecstatic to see their little girl doing so well, while I cried silently in the opening of the window and paneled blinds. Mom looked so fragile and weak and I couldn't help her. Nothing I could do would give her strength and, for the first time, I was forced to look down at the mercy killing, eyes peeled wide open and pinned to soft skin around my eye sockets like I saw once in a Tom & Jerry cartoon.

"Where's Vaughn?" Mom asked.

"He's—," Gram hesitated, "he's over by the window. He'll be back in a moment."

My grandmother rubbed her leg as she let me cry, watching my life fall around me in giant slabs of stone. If I knew any better and thought she was going to die for certain, I would've jumped right in front of one of the falling stones and let it crush me underneath its impossible weight. Instead, I left the masses to comfort Mom after she had her own, life-threatening masses extracted from her body.

"I love you, Mom," I bent over her bed after composing myself so I wouldn't cry all over her.

"I love you too, baby," her whispers were spectral, other worldly, but weak and poisoned. "It's going to be okay," she promised. "You're going to be amazing someday. I just know it."

Chapter Eighteen
SIBS

"How's your mom doing?" Trey text me as I lugged my bags into Aunt Mar's truck. We were heading out to my Aunt Barb's house in North Carolina for St. Patrick's Day with all of my dad's siblings. It wasn't the first time I had seen all of them since Dad passed away, but it was the first trip we'd ever taken together all at once.

"She's doing great! Watching the house while I'm away with my brother," I sent as I tried hiding my smile so Aunt Mar wouldn't ask what I was smirking about. All of my aunts and my uncle supported me on all fronts once Dad passed away. Aunt Mar and I became closest through it all. Dad never really engaged with his siblings that much. He always made plans and then would cancel last minute or just disappear. I knew how that was—our special power to shut people out, no matter who they were, and hide away. Dad and I were a lot alike on that front, but it was something I was working through since he passed.

"Good!" he replied, and I quickly sent a winking face to him.

"I'd like to see you when I get back, yeah?" I asked.

"For sure," he winked back and I bid him farewell with a kissing face as I looked up at the clear and beautiful March morning as we embarked for my uncle's home. Aunt Mel and Uncle Chris were waiting for us before we made the long drive down.

"Are you job searching?" Aunt Mar made sure to keep up on all the things I had to do. Sometimes I resented how much she was on my case. Deep down, I was thankful for it since I was one person at the helm of so much important shit that needed to be done and it all was time sensitive.

"Yeah, I am. Nothing quite yet. I can always head back to the Sheraton. They said they'd take me on, and I'd technically make comparable money there to what I made at the other hotel," I exasperatingly sighed.

"Hey, look. I think firing you for calling off well in advance to take care of stuff for your dad was shitty. They don't deserve a hard worker like you. Don't worry about it now. Let's just have a good time, yeah?" she grabbed my arm and squeezed lightly.

"I like that idea," I smiled as we sped along the highway toward my uncle's house. This was the second time I'd been away from the suffocating heaviness of my home. I didn't count New

Year's as the first because it was all still emotionally charged. The further from Dad's death I got, the further removed from the ache I could push myself. That didn't erase the pain but left a buffer so I was safe from it—almost like I threw it down a well and watched as it drowned, but it could grow limbs and crawl its way back to the surface to unexpectedly greet me in truly horrific fashion.

Our first stop was at a quiet rest stop just into Maryland. Aunt Mar and I took the backseat while Uncle Chris drove, and Aunt Mel was snack distributor in the passenger seat. It was an endless playlist of rock music, which wasn't my first choice, but Uncle Chris volunteered to drive the rental car all the way there and back, so he got to choose what station we listened to. Rightfully so, I think. His music reminded me of younger days of mine when they lived in a home in the middle of a field down a long stretch of quiet road. They had a pool in the backyard and plenty of space to run around and play with my two younger cousins. Their basement was where my Uncle Chris's and Aunt Kris's work stations were, where he'd burn Creed and Incubus and Hootie and the Blowfish CDs for my dad.

"We're stopping at the same rest stop, yeah?" Aunt Mel asked.

"That's the plan," Uncle Chris veered the car off the smooth exit ramp and into the first parking spot. Green covered over the small rest stop building where the bathrooms were, in front of a backdrop of long, golden fields, waiting to sprout green for the summer. It was chilly, but the sun beamed tingling warmth across my goosebump-covered arms.

"Guys, we need to get a photo like last time!" Aunt Mel turned excitedly back to the passenger seat as we started to exit the vehicle.

"Alright, alright, let me take a pee first," Aunt Mar started dancing as she made her way to the bathroom. Her and my dad were eerily alike on so many levels, it was kind of comforting.

Once back outside, we walked out toward one of the picnic benches and stood in front of it, trying to get a good photo of all of us.

"Let me take the photo," I offered and stepped away from the group since I wasn't there the last time they went down to North Carolina.

I could barely remember the last time I had been down to North Carolina, where a good chunk of family lived. It was years ago when I was a kid, but after Mom and Dad's divorce. He had a sliver Ford Ranger and drove that little trick into the ground. A thirteen hour drive in a two seated truck with no room to sprawl out had to be the most uncomfortable ride I've ever been in. Dad knew the Ranger wasn't a travel vehicle and, needless to say, that was the last long trip we took in that truck.

Now, fully grown and able to legally drink, our first stop once we got down to Emerald Isle was the bar my Aunt Barb and Uncle K owned called Island Time Tavern. It was probably the coolest place I've ever been to, and I was excited to get behind the bar and help out for St. Patrick's Day. On night one of our arrival, though, I drank more than I probably should have and played songs that reminded me of Dad, so he could be included in the momentous, rare occasion of having everyone underneath one roof. Reluctantly, I played Where Are You Going? again. It was further enough away not to sting as much when Dave sang the chorus inside the angular bar that looked out to a deck and peaceful canal.

It wasn't that song that made me cry this time, but another that I hadn't played since he died, or even before that unless Dad played it or sung it with the guitar. It was his song to me when I was first born, and he played it all the time. Arms Wide Open by Creed was the song he always dedicated to me when I was younger. Dad always sang it and played it on Sunday afternoons after we visited Kuhn's Market post church service. The light was dark in our home, but the sun shined brightly on my neighbor's homes until high noon when the sun finally reached our side of the street.

"Did you play this?" Aunt Mel walked up to me from the bar and stood in front of my line of sight.

"Yeah," I mumbled underneath the loud music and looked in her eyes as she smiled sadly, but hopeful, at me.

"He loved you a lot," she started to tear up as I did, a little inebriated and emotionally vulnerable, while I stood alone by a table in the middle of the bar. "But you know that."

"I do," I didn't' want to make a scene by wiping my eyes, but my tears simply wouldn't disappear like I wanted them to, so they streaked long down my face to the hairs of my beard. She walked around the table and embraced me in her arms as we hugged, where I could cry in private. Aunt Barb watched me from the bar, though, with a smile that radiated love all the way from where she stood.

Uncle Karl was busy in the back office of the bar, stocking the beer, while Aunt Mar and Uncle Chris drank with each other close to the emergency exit door of Island Time. I cried because of Dad, yeah, but it wasn't just because of him. It was because of the support from my family, whom I hadn't spent much time with as an adult. Family to whom I, unknowingly, followed in Dad's footsteps and didn't talk to that often. They were always there, though, waiting for when I'd visit or spend time with them. Each one of them helped me in more ways than I could ever repay and it birthed a new fear I wasn't ready to face yet. When would I have to mourn them? Would it be next year? Next month? Would I even be alive to see it? As much as Dad promised he would outlive me, I hoped that they would outlive me because the absence of their existence would hit harder than I would expect, and the guilt from years of unintentional seclusion would hang over my head like an ugly, broken umbrella. I struggled with habitually thinking about what life would be like without the people I loved and held close to me—family, friends, and lovers alike. I wasn't sure if it was normal or a phase humans went through when someone close to them passes. Were these thoughts, these fears of mine, even normal? I remember texting my Psychology of Death & Dying professor about what was normal thinking or not. Politely, she apologized because she hadn't saved my number and she asked who I was. Quickly, and with as much focus as I could possibly muster while being way too buzzed to ask serious questions, I reintroduced myself to her and hoped she would remember. Bless her for understanding my drunken texts, but she gracefully pointed me to grief counseling and management professionals for this. It wasn't the answer I wanted, but the answer I most likely needed.

"You're one of us now. The sibs!" Aunt Barb laughed as she held out her arms before we ventured off to the beach for a couple of photos. The weather was still chilly, unfortunately, but it was the first time I was at the beach since James and I went last year to the Dominican Republic.

"Yeah," I laughed and stuffed my hands into my pockets.

"Sib Vaughn," she called me and I belly laughed because it sounded ridiculous. It was ridiculous, but I loved everything about it, being a part of this club and family. They were the best foundation and support system I could have never asked for or expected. That trip was full of a lot of great and warm feelings that filled me back up, brought me back to this cold, almost lifeless and jobless existence back in Pittsburgh—my post-apocalyptic life that I managed to stumble through the warzone battered and damaged, but not dead.

The hope they gave was what I focused on moving forward. It was every and any life preserve I'd ever needed moving forward as we left to go back home for our extended weekend. I had no job, no dad, a mother still recuperating from having a lobe of her lung extracted from her body, a brother and sister with drinking problems who I still loved anyways, and an extended family I had only begun coming to know in secret behind the sibs' backs. There was more than the hard-life-shit that boiled to the surface. I had this beautiful family, every last one of them, that stood by me through it all, and there is nothing I could ever say or ever do to show how thankful I was for that.

Chapter Nineteen
TREY

Trey and I planned our first hangout on the last snow-storm of the season, nearing the beginning of April. He was sig-nificantly taller than me, especially in person, and I thankfully had the house to myself so we wouldn't be bothered by Brian or Mom.

I raved about this show on Netflix, The OA, and told Trey how much he'd like it, so that was our plan for the day—to binge watch as much of the show as possible in one sitting.

When he arrived at my house, he did what any new visitor to the house would do and parked awkwardly behind my vehicle on the steep hill of Dad's home. Everything was covered in snow, but the weather was no match for his Subaru and he made it up just fine to park. Mom was collecting her things to leave as I gushed about how amazing Trey was though we hadn't even really met yet. I ran down the stairs like a weirdo, jogged through the basement to the entryway door, and let him inside so he wasn't covered in falling snow.

"Well, hey you," we hugged tightly in the laundry room before I showed him the way upstairs.

"Don't mind the mess down here," I stopped so he could take off his shoes.

"Oh, don't worry about it. It's a basement," he laughed at my worry.

"Also, this was totally not the purpose, but you're accidentally going to meet my mom so, surprise?" I laughed uneasily.

"Sure it wasn't," he teased me and made my stomach flip over itself. Truth be told, it was an honest accident—some mishap where she was running late for a doctor's appointment or to go see Pap. I can't remember.

"Oh shush," I laughed as we slowly walked up the stairs to the main floor where Mom collected her things and started for the dining room.

"Mom, this is Trey. Trey, this is my mom," I motioned back and forth to them, and saw immediately by the look on my mom's face that she already liked him.

"Hi! Sorry I'm here. I'm running a little late on my way out the door."

"Don't worry about it. How're you feeling? Vaughn told
me about your procedure," Trey leaned against the kitchen table
and stared directly into her eyes, enthralled in their brief conversation. Everything quieted in that moment. I watched him talk to
my mom, studied how the light reflected off his black and grey-
streaked hair and how his eyes reflected the soft white light that
burst through the kitchen window by the stove and cutting board.
When he smiled, bright white teeth reflected the same light his
eyes. His laugh was the sound of your favorite color.

"Well, it was lovely meeting you, Vaughn's mom," he held
out his hand to shake.

"Oh, no. We hug in this house," Mom looked so tiny com-
pared to his height. We were tiny people in this family of ours.
Trey did this weird "Well, sure," thing with his mouth and squinted his eyes in the biggest smile.

"I'm all about hugs," Trey laughed some more before they
departed and she left to go run her errands.

"Be careful, Ma. Love you," I yelled from the top of the
basement stairs.

"I will! Have fun!" she yelled from the bottom of the stairs
as she put on her shoes.

"Well, that was my mom," I shrugged.

"She's a sweetheart," he smiled sincerely.

"Yeah, I'm obsessed with her. She's amazing," I gushed as
I lingered slowly toward him into the kitchen. "Are you thirsty?"

"Water would be great," he swallowed hard and leaned
against the counter my microwave sat on. Dad never nailed it into
the top of the drawers so it slid almost off the top when he leaned
against it. "Oh shit, I broke something," Trey awkwardly moved
the top of the counter so it realigned with the drawer.

"Oh, don't worry about the counter. It was never screwed in anyways," my face flashed red as he tapped the top of the microwave like it was a pet. "Did you want to start watching the show? Do you want popcorn?"

"No popcorn for me," he looked back over at the microwave and took the glass of water I poured for him.

"Alright," I hesitated, walking by him while we stood there in my kitchen. "Okay, so, I'm going to apologize in advance. My bedroom is the only place where the television works. Downstairs doesn't have Netflix or cable."

"Sure," he raised his eyebrow. "You just want to get me into your bed."

"Oh my goodness," my face flushed red and the room spun for three long seconds. "No, no. I promise."

"It's alright," he laughed. "I'm only joking. Let's head on upstairs."

He led the way and I directed him to my bedroom. Before he came over, I cleaned so he wouldn't judge me for how dirty my room was. I wasn't able to dust everything before he came over and I fixated on it until the show started.

"Okay, it's hard to get into at first. A lot of stuff happens all at once, but it gets so good," I cuddled next to him—body pressed against body as his arm stretched around my shoulders and pulled me into him closer. I felt my heart creep into my throat and swallowed hard, but the tightness never went away. His hand traced down my arm to my hand, running up and down each finger while we watched The OA. It was a good thing I'd watched the entire first season so many times by that point so I could focus on not screaming from the warmth in his touch, or in the gentle, heart-swelling moments he'd tear up and sniffle at whatever was happening on the television. *Why is he even here, in this house, in my bedroom, and in my bed with me? There is nothing special about me. Does he want to be here or is this pity? What are his thoughts of me? Am I doing something stupid? Does he hate the way we're laying here?* He was in much better shape than me and I looked like an uninteresting gelatin mold.

"Are you okay?" he shook me out of my rapid cycle thinking and into the present, where all of those questions didn't matter. Trey had been there from afar through everything, since he reached out after Dad died. He didn't care about any of that. He wasn't that person, at least from what I knew about him. The parts of his soul he showed me were the most beautiful, they suffocated him in radiant golden light that he never kept to himself but shared with the others around him. It was light that he shared with me because that was what his soul looked like.

"I'm great!" I leaned down onto his chest and felt the way his heart beat against my ear, how it sounded when he breathed in and out, in slow paced cycles that made my heart swell.

"Hey," he gently shook me so I looked at him.

"Yeah—?"

As I turned to look at him, he pulled me closer into him, so our hearts beat together, synced for only seconds as we looked into each other's eyes. Deeper and deeper I fell into them, lost in a beautiful bright brown that I'd never seen in anyone else's before that moment. So, I did what I felt I wanted to, because if I'd learned anything in those short couple of months at all, it was that we are never guaranteed any amount of time or space, so love who you want, kiss without fear, and be exactly what terrifies you. Unless that terrifying thing is a serial killer, bank robber, or any other terrible thing. Don't be that.

I kissed him like nothing else mattered, because it didn't. Once we parted, Trey kissed me back like I was the last person on this earth he would ever kiss.

We slept for hours and missed half of the show. When we woke up from our unexpected nap, Netflix asked, *Are you still watching?*

"Shit, what time is it?" he jumped up and out of bed. The white light reflected off the freshly fallen snow ignited his naked back in a warm, soft light that I felt right through my soul.

"Six, I think," I grumbled and rolled over to look at my phone. "Yep, 6:13 p.m."

"Fuck. I was supposed to meet my friends for dinner," he got up and threw on his shirt quickly, trying to brush out the wrinkles with his hands.

"Sounds fun! Sorry to keep you for so long. I didn't expect to fall asleep," I wrapped the blankets around my body as he looked outside and fell onto the bed in surprise.

"So much snow, oh my goodness," his face turned like he'd tasted something sour.

"Yeah? I'm over it," I sighed in a tired laugh.

"Want to come with me?" he asked.

"Where?" I didn't want to assume he meant to dinner, so I asked knowing that was the only thing it could possibly be, unless he wanted to go out into the snow.

"To dinner tonight, so you can meet my friends?" he set his hand on my leg, hidden underneath warm grey blankets.

"Really?" I asked.

"I don't just go napping with everyone, you know," Trey winked at me and tapped my leg before standing again. "Get ready so we can head out, yeah?" he stretched, and his hands touched the ceiling of the bedroom. If I was going to be awake enough to meet his friends and not be an awkward potato, I desperately needed coffee intravenously injected into my body.

We drove through the heavy, wet snow in his Subaru to Shady Grove, a pizza joint in the beautiful but gentrified Shadyside area of Pittsburgh. Along Walnut, a small little strip of road that mimicked Pittsburgh's beautiful Sewickley area, Shady Grove sat tucked across from high-end clothing stores, a Mad Mex, and a hot yoga studio on the second floor below apartment units. His friend Cory and his boyfriend sat in the darkest corner in the back of the restaurant by the jukebox. Trey led the way as I hid behind his figure. I tried everything to remain inconspicuous and hidden so they couldn't eye me up just yet, until I was close enough to see them both. My nerves fired off in a million little fireworks inside my brain. Everything felt so hot while I sat at the table next to Trey, desperately needing a drink to loosen me up and drown out my anxiety. They weren't mean people at all. Simply, I wanted them to like me, so everything felt so important to me.

Unbeknownst to Trey, I was three shakes away from a full-blown anxiety attack. Tunnel vision closed in quickly as they chatted and talked and I buried myself in unending silence and over-thought. Then, his hand reached for mine underneath the table, squeezed lightly, and every ounce of anxiety that swallowed me up disappeared in one bright crack of lightning inside my head that reverberated through my ribcage. Everything was okay. I was alright, safe, and perfectly fine, and it was all communicated by the gentle squeeze of his hand. This thing between Trey and I could live and be good. I could have this one truly great moment if I let myself believe in it. I believed in it. I believed in it like I had nothing to lose. I had nothing to lose.

It was a partly sunny day. Or maybe partly cloudy? I never could tell the difference. I shifted above and below cloud nine because of the mental destruction left from everything with my dad and my crumbling family behind the scenes. Every day I woke, it was a new altitude, while I tried so desperately to rest on top of that cloud for as long as I could. Each time I tried, I'd overshoot or sink beneath overwhelm, where my sickness, the ghost that lingered inside my head, drowned me further into the dark spaces labeled depression and anxiety.

I was mid-shift at my credit reporting job—a job Trey had been so excited about me getting since I had lost my last job in the flash-bang beginning of our relationship. It was any other day at the monotonous call center. It was kind of nice, though, since I spent an entire month off of work for the first time since I started working at sixteen. Since we dealt with secured financial information, cell phone use was forbidden. I broke that rule every day. It didn't really matter, to be honest, because my managers liked me and I worked my ass off to move up quickly for that extra buck in my pocket.

"I'm so sorry," the text read from someone I wouldn't call a friend but an unfortunate acquaintance.

"What?" I asked. They had ties to John, so I assumed something happened to him or they just figured out my dad passed six months and three days after it had already happened. This person knew from photos on Facebook, though, so that couldn't be it.

"You don't know?" he replied in seconds.

"No, I don't. What are you talking about?" I sent back, but in the time it took him to reply, I got a call on the phone from a consumer ready to yell in my ear about why a credit inquiry from our company appeared on their credit report. As I motioned through the same monotonous spiel about who we were and why we would show up on a credit report, my phone buzzed twice against my grey dress pants, wrapped tightly around my body. For a split second, I pulled my phone out while the consumer on the phone ranted and searched through their records. The bright screen on my phone illuminated the dark space I hid it underneath the desk and in between my legs, so I could hide from the camera and my manager's eyes. I squinted at the news article link, wildly unsure of what I was looking at, till I recognized the car.

Blue Subaru shoved underneath the back of an eighteen-wheeler. Glass covered the sour, night-dripped highway with flashing police lights and orange sodium exit ramp lights caught in still life. A white sheet was dragged from the driver-side window to the passenger side window, hiding everything on the inside. The caption read: Fatal Crash Shuts Down Parkway East.

I clicked on the link with uncontrollably shaky hands and skimmed through nonsense at the beginning of the article from a local news station.

"It happened around 11:15 p.m. in the eastbound lanes, near the Squirrel Hill-Homestead exit. State Police say a car was traveling east when it struck a tractor-trailer from behind. The back of the trailer sliced through the car's front windshield and sheared off nearly half of its roof. The driver of the car was pronounced dead at the scene. He has been identified as Walter "Trey" Goff III, 28, of Pittsburgh."

"Hello?" The caller yelled at me. "Are you listening?"

"I uh—," I hung up the call, and ran from my cubicle toward the escape. The office walls closed in, crumbled around me, ready to bury me alive and suffocate me until I was dead. I pressed the elevator button about a hundred times but it never showed. As I stumbled toward the stairwell door, other workers in different departments stared at me like I was a maniac or drunk. *This is a dream. That isn't real.*

My feet caught twice on the stairs, but my hand caught the handrail just in time, so I wouldn't fall. I sucked in air, rampantly and shaken. The ground vibrated underneath my feet like the entire floor was cooked spaghetti noodles and I burst through the heavy fire door, sprinted out to the front of the building, and kneeled onto the ground.

"Please, God. Don't do this to me. I can't do this again. There's nothing left in me. Take me instead but leave him. I don't want to have to get over him. Please, God, damnit!" I screamed out in the front of the building without a care in the world whether others saw me from inside or not. I don't know why but I Face Timed my roommate, Samantha.

"Hey, what's up?" she asked as she sat in her bed with bright, brilliant light shining behind her.

"I uh—I don't know how—I don't know how to say this."

"What is it? Are you okay?" she sat up in her bed as she squinted and pulled the phone closer to her face.

"Trey died."

Trey died. I never thought I'd hear myself say those words. Ever. I felt separated from my body but trapped in a cage where I was being ruthlessly tortured, praying for any kind of escape. I prayed for a piano to fall on my head, for a stray bullet to pass through my heart or head. I prayed for a car to hit me, for my heart to explode within my chest so I'd finally stop breathing. I didn't care if it was violent. I couldn't do this again. Not yet, not so soon. Not six months and three days after my dad had passed.

Please, God. Take me instead.

IRIS

Chapter Twenty
MEMORIAL

I wrote our story like a fairytale, not for dramatic effect, but because it was a fairytale for me. It was a fairytale for you, too, because you hurt somewhere deep down, and we shared that pain together as well as the desire to heal each other. I loved you with every fiber of my being, even the damaged pieces that you understood and accepted so easily. You were the curse that none of us saw coming, sweetly wrapped in bright and shiny paper, stamped as a blessing when you appeared in my life. Through the ups, though, there were soaring and striking downs that I ignored when I first started writing about our flash-in-a-pan.

It started when you told me you could possibly no longer be in Pittsburgh if you got this dream job down in Virginia. I'd just found you. I wasn't going to lose you that easily.

"I'll go with you," I protested as you pulled away and fought against my lack of will to stay. I had nothing here that I loved more than you—nothing to anchor me here other than sour and sore memories of my dad and everything he touched in my world. I lived in a home that pushed me down into depressed, black and purple waters—water that sucked into my lungs and turned into thick glue or scorched tar.

"You don't even know me," he argued.

"I don't care, Trey. I like what I see already, and you know why I don't mind leaving so easily. I can't be here in this city without you. I don't want to be here in this city without you. We'd function so well together, and even if you weren't ready to give up sleeping on your own, I'd sleep in a different room or something. Anything. I'd do anything if you'd just let me."

"I can't let you do that. You can't choose that, Vaughn. We barely know each other!" Trey argued.

"I don't care, Trey. It's my choice. I want to follow you and be with you. Please, let me do that."

"What if I don't want that?" he pushed the knife right into my chest as I thought about every time our lips formed to each other's. I thought about the time we cooked dinner in his kitchen and he told me to put on my favorite music to cook to: it was a Madeleine Peyroux song called *J'ai Deux Amours*. When Trey pulled me from incorrectly chopping the carrots for our pork roast and turned me around. When he gently breathed in and pulled me closer into his chest. He was so tall that I fit perfectly into him, his heart right in my earshot. As Peyroux sang the chorus, the slow and soft beat of a hardtop rattling in the background behind a softened, jazzy piano, we danced in the middle of his kitchen until the song ended. Where I was euphoric in the first taste of light since my dad passed, Trey introduced the possible nuclear winter that could not only sear every bright memory of us but cover it in white overlay particle.

"You can't just push me out and away. What was this supposed to be then? Fun? Did you just decide one day that you didn't want to be with me? Did I do something wrong? Was it because I said I'd go with you? You don't understand what you mean to me. It's not fair that you're pushing me away and not even letting the possibility of our future live. You're trying to kill it and everything else in your path. Why?" Trey left me in the dark for days with zero communication. I texted him a couple *I miss you's* and long-winded paragraphs when my anxiety and depression backed me into a corner. I was ready to tap out. I didn't want to live in a world without Trey in my life. I pushed him out of my walls. *Me.* This was my fault and I had no say in how the dice landed. I think that was the worst feeling, as I scrolled through our love-soaked messaged and tormented myself in every waking moment. I missed him before he died—before our first separation.

I wasn't perfect then. I don't think there will ever be a time when I will be perfect for anyone, but you were my perfect—the love that got away not once, but twice. It was an intensity I never fully understood, though, either. Was it because you saved me from the ultimate pain of losing my dad? Was it how you softened the blow when his absence became omnipotent and controlled every thought and feeling? Or was it that we actually had this deeper, emotional current that electrified us like a drug we couldn't get enough of because our souls sang the most incredible song when they were together. I was in the dark space that screamed out from my chest like water splashing against volcanic rock ripe with orange veins where smoldering lava ebbed and flowed beneath.

I sat at his memorial at the PERSAD Center in Pittsburgh's Lawrenceville district, my back against a wall of windows that let in golden light into the neutral colored room. My friend, Julie, came with me. I'd driven to her house the day I found out Trey died because I didn't trust myself alone. While we sat there during his best friends' speeches, I lost myself in a constant ringing inside my ears while I rolled over in my head the last time I saw Trey and what it was like.

We hadn't seen each other for at least a month. Fresh scabs glowed soft pink and ugly dark yellow around my heart from the damage he left me in to clean up on my own. It was May 14th, the day I planned to celebrate my birthday—the first birthday I'd have without Dad. To do something a little different, I wanted to throw a roaring twenties themed party, where we'd all dress up in theatrical clothes and spend a night out on the town, hopping around speakeasy-style bars. A part of me wasn't sure if I could handle inviting him to the party, but I did anyways on Facebook, and he messaged me immediately about how it was the day before his exam, so he couldn't be out late, but he'd be there.

We met for dinner in Market Square at Diamond Market, where they had the best bourbon burgers. Trey and I sat inside at a table against the large front windows of the restaurant. He was in his best vest and I wore a near-matching one.

"So," I smiled big as I admired everything about him. "How've you been?"

"Oh, you know," he laughed and smiled bigger than I'd seen him smile before. "Didn't get the job, which is okay, but I test to get certified as a therapist tomorrow! Which is exciting, but terrifying. I didn't study," he cackled loudly, making a self-depre-cating joke about himself. "Oh well. Tell me about YOU! It's your birthday."

"There's not much to really bring you up to speed on. Family is kind of in shambles—Brian and Chelsey aren't really talking much anymore. I met my siblings that I didn't even know I had recently! It was amazing. Probably one of the best moments for me, for sure."

"That's awesome!"

"Yeah, it was really great," we bantered back and forth while we drank weird beer and ate lukewarm food. The evening was still young, mostly, but our check sitting at the edge of the table felt like it sped time up way faster than I wanted it to. I wanted to hold his hand across from him at the table. While I tried holding my breath so I didn't look like a bloated potato, I wanted to kiss him and hug him for all the moments I wanted to and couldn't within the past month. I held back, though, and he generously picked up the bill as a birthday present to me.

"Oh! Before I forget," he reached into his back pocket and pulled out this misshapen rock.

"What?" I laughed loudly, completely enamored by how goofy he was yet disarmingly charming. "Is that your emotional support rock?" I teased.

"Very funny," he winked back with a huge smile and handed it to me. "While I was hiking last weekend out by my mom's house, I saw this rock and it reminded me of you and your birthday coming up, so I picked it up to give to you."

"No one's given me a rock before," I studied every surface, both jagged and smooth, as I rolled it around in my hand. What reminded him of me in this rock? Was it the shift in browns along the surface or the way the edges smoothed out and sharpened in mismatched patterns? "I absolutely love it. It's perfect. Thanks, Trey," I spoke low enough that only he could hear me.

"I'm glad!" Trey sighed like he'd held his breath the entire time I studied the gift.

We walked from the restaurant to the courtyard in front of the Omni William Penn Hotel. The fountains misted watery whispers in the illuminated pools and walkways. We sat on a cold metal bench, close next to each other to keep warmth, and stared at the hotel together.

"What do you want to talk about?" I asked.

"Anything you want. It's your birthday," he spoke.

"Okay," I sighed tiredly as a million questions flashed through my head. I didn't want this to be a fight. I just wanted closure so I could begin my healing. I didn't want to be as long-winded as the texts he'd ignored countless times over again in the time he blocked me out of existence. "I don't want to make you upset. I just feel like there wasn't any closure and that's what I'm hung up on. You know?"

"Totally," he whispered in a shiver.

"I'm not angry with you at all. I've accepted you don't want to date me and that's totally okay. It doesn't change the fact that I—," everything inside my body screamed the word love but I held it back and stumbled over my words in desperate search for another one. "I really liked you and you were the first lightness I've felt for so long. That's not your fault, though. You couldn't control the time you entered into my life and it wasn't fair to you. I mean, you clearly know how I feel about you with all those messages I sent you," I joked at my own expense to make him laugh and lighten the conversation.

"No, totally. I really didn't want to ignore those. I never, in a million years, wanted to hurt you. I think you're a phenomenal person, but people like you scare me."

"What do you mean?" I tried to hide the hurt and shake in my voice.

"You're so passionate, and you were so ready to sacrifice everything you had here for me and it put me into a completely different headspace because it was so soon and there was so much at stake that a new relationship shouldn't have. It's supposed to be about learning from each other and about each other, farting comfortably in front of each other and watching terrible movies together," we laughed together as our joint cackles felt like they echoed off the side of the giant buildings encompassing us.

"Yeah, you're right," I sighed and rubbed my arms together to warm up. "I just don't want you to think I don't want you in my life. I care tremendously about you, more than I expected from myself. That's something I need to work on, though. I can't be what I want to be with you because you don't want that."

"I don't want a relationship with you."
I wish he hadn't said what I already knew because it stung just as badly as if I'd heard it for the first time in that courtyard.

"I know," I fixated on the gently swaying American flag in front of the Omni William Penn Hotel. "I'm okay with that. I just need time to sort my feelings out for you so I can learn to be your friend."

"I understand that," he rubbed his hands together and looked over at me. I let myself fall against him in a gentle lean against his shoulder.

"You're an incredible person, you know that? In whatever capacity you'll be in my life, I'll be happy. I just have to heal a little bit longer."

"I can respect that," he leaned his head against mine before we got up to leave. "So, what do you want me to do?" He asked in regard to another drink at the speakeasy bar I was late for meeting my friends at.

"You should go home and get some rest for your test," I smiled at him as he stretched and stared directly into my eyes.

"So, no bar?" he asked.

"I feel good with this celebration of ours, here. Plus, with alcohol, I don't really trust myself with you being around."

"Fair, fair!" he laughed and pulled me in for a hug.

"Thank you for the rock. It was the best gift I've ever gotten. Honestly," I whispered into his ear with my head propped and strained on his shoulder. I shifted my view to the side and leaned into his chest to hear his heartbeat. It was warm, alive, and radiant against my ear, and it steadied the quick flash of heat throughout my body. I missed his smell, the way he felt so close, how his heartbeat sounded in my ear, and the way he'd speak sweet nothings in Spanish I never understood to me. I missed everything that we were and our brief moment in beautiful time and it made me never want to let go of him. I never wanted to end that moment. We pulled away and he kissed me on the cheek.

"Happy birthday, mio lindo."

"Thanks, Trey," I squeezed his hand and we parted ways, our backs turned to each other as we walked in opposite directions. Turn around. Tell him to come back. I felt the words and desires sear inside my chest. I turned, ready to yell out at him to stay instead of leaving and watched as the walkway lights lit him in beautiful bright white as he walked down the stairs and disappeared into view. "I love you," I whispered in my aloneness. That would be, unbeknownst to me, the last time I'd ever see Trey.

"Does anyone else want to speak?" one of Trey's best friends, Ryan, asked at the microphone. Julie nudged my arm with her elbow as my sweaty hand gripped the rock Trey had given me for my birthday a little over a month ago.

"Me!" I felt the word vomit from the pit of my stomach. The roomful of heads turned to look over at the small, awkward guy who yelled in nervous, unsteady laughter. I walked up to the podium as the room stiffened into a quiet unease that triggered my anxiety. Change your mind. It's not too late. *Who are you to speak at his memorial? These people don't even know who you are. What could you possibly have to say about him that's important? You hadn't spoken to him in at least a month.*

"Hi, everyone," I choked at the microphone podium in front of the white screen cycling photos of Trey. "So," I paused when my anxiety crawled into my throat and blocked my breathing. This was not the time to choke and give out. "Trey reached out to me for the first time as a total stranger less than a week after my Dad had died. It was a short six months and three days before Trey passed that he had reached out to me in my darkest moment. He brought the most brilliant and incredible light that, quite honestly, kept me alive when I didn't want to be..." I began with the memory of his heartbeat in my ear. For the first time in my entire life, all the way back to my first memory of feeling mental illness take control of my body as a little kid, I was the one in control of my mental illness.

Chapter Twenty-One
DEAD DADS CLUB

My dad wasn't the first one to pass among us in this little group I'd dubbed the Dead Dads Club. It wasn't a club anyone wanted to be a part of. There were no crazy admission tests or criteria, per se, other than the obvious title. Three girls whom I graduated with lost their fathers just like me. It seemed wildly coincidental that we would all be from the same grade, fairly close to each other at one point or another and all going through the same loss.

Before the inception of the group, we had watched each other struggle and hurt through Facebook posts, going through that continual stream of love and thoughtfulness as each of us shared our loss publicly through our social media accounts. Individually, we reacted to each of our posts as we did what we had to do to move forward with our lives, so we weren't stagnant and trapped in the grief. I don't really remember who started the messenger group. I think it was Emily, who I considered to be my sister from another mister.

My history with Emily went way back to middle school.

There was a brief moment in time when my mom and I had to evacuate our low-income apartment because of severe black mold problems that greatly affected Mom's breathing. She wasn't sure where to have us go, or if I'd be able to stay in the West Allegheny School District. Kept in heavily guarded secret from the school, I briefly moved in with Emily and her parents, so I could stay in the district while my mom hopped around from friend's house to friend's house before we found our own home. I spent months sleeping in the bedroom next door to Emily. My temporary yellow room with floral patterns and two big mirrored closet doors reflected the light from the high windows. Stuffed animals covered the bed, but they disappeared shortly after when Emily's mom realized it was a little less masculine for a growing teen. Sometimes, I'd sleep in their solarium because I liked to watch television before I went to sleep back then, and Emily and I could chat through her window after her mom went to bed.

Our mother's bonded pretty well and they did more than just give me a place to stay in those haphazard years. I became family as they took me to Easter lunches out at golf resorts, stayed on top of my schooling so I wouldn't fall behind, and provided the least stressful home environment so I could focus on my schoolwork and not the stresses of not having a place to call home. I felt orphaned and uneasy anyways. It was at no fault to Emily or her parents because they gave me everything. Emily and I became unofficial brother and sister as we laughed, explored, and even argued.

Middle school was weird times for everyone, honestly. It was the most traumatic time as a growing child and everything means so much even if, in the grand scheme of things, it wasn't a big deal. Thinking back on it, with my deep obsession with Cirque Du Soleil and Imogen Heap at their peak, it was slightly hilarious

that Em's mom didn't know I was gay. It was fairly obvious, looking back now. I'd never admit it back then. I didn't have the balls
to self-proclaim the identity I was bullied for at school every day
just yet.

For the first time in a long time, Emily and her parents
showed me what a normal life was supposed to be. There was no
divorce carnage to shift through, no eggshell family drama to tip-
toe across, or anxiety or worry about if we'd eat this week or not.
Mom and I didn't go visit the food pantry for that time and riding
the short bus wasn't all as bad as it was cracked up to be. They
showed me how life could be, how it should be, and I don't think I
could thank them enough for the brief taste of relief I hadn't felt
since before the divorce.

Emily unexpectedly lost her dad like I had. After we graduated, and even through high school, we drifted apart but tried to
visit each other often enough to keep in touch. Life happens after
high school ends. We drifted apart like most friends do after you
don't spend eight hours a day in the same building. Once I heard
she lost her dad, it was a mournful pain that ached in the center of
my bones because he was just as much as acquired family as Emily
was to me. We had talks about life and sports (it was a struggle)
during breakfast in the morning, talked about goals and desires
at their glass table in their kitchen. They celebrated my birthday
more than once on that glass table and her father was there for it,
too. Emily and I became closer once he passed and started to do all
the things we said we were going to do before graduation—hang
out, keep in touch, explore, and live life in brief moments together.

Jaymie's dad passed slowly over time—another person who
I had known somewhat closely, but not as close as Emily's parents.
It was the same illness that threatened my mom's life. His battle

against cancer was long but he was strong and resilient. Jaymie and her beautiful family shared their dad's journey on Facebook and I followed along and supported from afar because death was reckless in this short year for the Dead Dads Club. Jaymie and I went way back to middle school and stayed friends throughout high school.

I was known to shift friend groups, keeping my circle very large because I liked everyone and wanted to make people happy. She was a part of the musical theater group of friends as we'd get cast in shows together, get assigned duets for small little performances throughout the year. I geeked out every time her and I had to sing together because she had a set of incredible pipes and she made me feel like I could sing stronger and come out of the thick, shy tar pool I made a home in throughout my high school years. We spent nights watching endless amounts of Halloween movies over her house in the same trailer park I lived in, across from the high school. They'd decorate the outside and the inside and it was incredible. Her family invited me to pumpkin patch days, where her dad would drive us out to a local farm in Clinton. Her dad also picked us up from marching band practice some nights in their Astro van I'd dubbed the "party van." We had plans to go on a road trip in that van someday—something that never came to fruition.

Morgan's dad passed away abruptly. I wasn't really close to her in high school or middle school. There were a few moments I could recollect in high school where I did something stupid and made her laugh in the hallway or lunch period. She was a quiet person. Regardless, I was glad we could become close. I wish we had become close under different circumstances, but Emily, Jaymie, and I welcomed her into our group with wide open arms and hearts. Morgan's relationship with her dad mirrored a lot of my relationship with my dad. It hit home hard. More than that, though, it opened my eyes that I really wasn't alone in my specific grief.

The Dead Dads Club met for the first time with all four members at Panera Bread. We didn't spend much time talking about what happened to our fathers. This was a time to be supportive of our life endeavors, catch up, rant about the stupid little things that seem even smaller now that we live with grief hung inside our ribcages, and mentioned some things about how our lives were continually affected by the loss even after everyone else moved on from it. That was the hardest part for me—when everyone else was done with their grief while I was still in the thick of it.

There was no way to escape from it, especially being administrator of Dad's estate. Everything fell on my shoulders, but I selfishly chose to be the administer because I didn't trust anyone, not even my own family at some points. We were all in the thick of our grief and pressured to keep moving forward when all we wanted to do was have life stop for a moment to breathe, forget to remember, remember to forget, and then move forward when it felt right. Life doesn't allow that. Especially for the grieving.

We gained two unexpected members shortly after, Taylor and Meg. Their loss was a little different than ours, though, but just as hard to swallow. Taylor and I hung out for the first time since high school months before he unexpectedly lost his mom. We went to grab food downtown one evening to chat and catch up. I think we matched on Tinder at one point, which is how it all came down to us meeting up. Food turned to drinks with his friend Mary in the Strip District of Pittsburgh. Mary was ready to go home after drinking, though, and Taylor and I had some energy left in us to party.

"Let's go somewhere and dance," he said as we walked down Smallman Street.

"There are really only two places I can think of," I shook from the chill in the air as we walked through dark streets, closer to the city. "Cruze or Lucky's."

"Lucky's," he started running toward the bar, laughing, as I tried catching up to him. Out of breath and incredibly out of shape, we arrived at Lucky's and walked in to the dimly lit bar with giant mirrors on the bar wall. "Dancing is upstairs."

"You've been here before?" I asked.

"Once or twice," he grabbed my hand after we got a drink and led me to the second floor where naked men danced on the square bar while the bartenders poured drinks below them.

"I don't know how I'd feel about getting a drink from up here while the strippers danced over my drink," I tried to joke but the music was so loud, my voice was lost in it. Taylor and I went to the farthest corner of the dance floor just before the light disappeared into shadow. The beat shook my ribcage, my alcoholic buzz vibrated behind my eyes and intensified with the lights that flashed and roamed around the crowd of onlookers. We started dancing without a care in the world about who watched us. We danced until we dissolved into the flashing lights, overheated, with our coats still on for whatever reason. It was freeing and radical and electric. We were two friends who didn't care for an hour of a random night all because we matched on Tinder. It was weird—*the best* kind of weird that makes you smile.

Meg and I weren't close in high school. She shared a friendship with another friend of mine, but we hadn't really been close-close at all. Meg lost her mom, unexpectedly I believe, but she had kept it quite private and I admired that about her. It took insurmountable strength to keep that pain muted.

The Dead Parents* Club was more than just friends who all graduated together in the same class and lost someone close to them. We were acquired family and a support system that existed outside of the radius of our personal grief. We could shoot off a message to the group one day and get support almost instantaneously when our strength wavered. It wasn't often that we met or if at all since we were healing as we moved forward for the sake of survival. It didn't mean there was a day that went by when they weren't on my mind. This little club, a huge lifeline of mine, existed through the fallout and ash of a barely breathing moment in my life. We survived and continued forward, not because we had to, because we had each other to inspire and cheer up when the days were overcast and the end of the clouds were nowhere in sight.

Chapter Twenty-Two
BEYOND THESE WALLS

"You'll always have this house to come home to."
Dad's words put a bitter metallic taste in my mouth as I let that same house fall into shambles from the inside out. It was never my home, no matter how many times he told me that when he was alive. *"I want you to have a home base you know you can come back to if life ever gets rocky,"* he would lecture when we'd see each other after long weeks of work. I put it up for sale a couple months after he passed away.

There were bigger dreams I had for Dad's house. I wanted to keep it in the family and live out the dream he had for it, me included. There were so many memories that needed to live in that house still, memories that would never fully flesh out because this wasn't a golden and untouchable safe space after he died. It was a burial ground, stained like burgundy wine on white lace. Memories of many lifetimes lived inside with family, long summer nights, cold winter days, my first birthday party, and his dead body laying flat on the green carpet, half in a body bag, haunted those halls in an endless state of delirium. Moments when my family faltered, cried, and screamed at each other in drunken stupors flashed against the beige carpet of the living and dining rooms. Nights when I cried and cried in the bathtub with a candle as my only light and hoped the steam from the shower beating against my reddened skin would enter in my lungs and drown me from the inside.

"We can save the place. You don't have to sell it at all," Brian pleaded both drunken and sober. I watched as he shook in anger and panic when I'd stare him down and tell him to get over the fact I was letting the house go. "This is not what Dad wanted at all."

"He's dead, Brian. I have to do what's best for me, alright? I can't be here anymore. I don't' want to live in a house where I'm depressed every time I have to come back to it or sleep here. I don't have to live that way," I argued.

"Keep it and let me stay there then. I'll pay the mortgage down and then you will have a free home and it'll help everyone."

"No, that's too much responsibility I don't need. I don't trust you enough to pay it quite honestly."

"Wow, dude. That's fucked up. Fuck you," he slammed the kitchen door to go smoke before he had to leave for work.

"Fuck me," I stood in the middle of the dining room and swayed from foot to foot. I let every hateful word burn holes into my body and permanently change the way my heart was shaped. "I don't need you," anger flashed behind my eyes before I retreated to my dusty bedroom—dust that covered the desk, television, and carpet. I watched as he left the house for work, dressed in all black because that was all he wore, and tapped through the phone I added to my plan so that he had something for emergencies. My brother would be the second person I'd kick out of the house in less than a year. Family or not, I wanted him out and gone forever.

"You need to move by the end of the month," I gave his sentence as he disappeared from view, into a line of trees that sat along the road leading to our home.

Chelsey didn't approve of selling the house either, but she was more removed from the everyday life of it than Brian was. My sister had a horrible habit of secluding herself in her own mind while she created scenarios that weren't even true. For instance, how Brian and I were abandoning her and purposefully leaving her out of things we did. It was different because she lived twenty minutes away at the very least, and Brian slept in the bedroom right next door to mine. Also, she had a drinking problem that my psyche couldn't help her through. I really did miss hanging with my sister and wanted to include her in anything I could because it made it better. For unintentional reasons, I had left her out of the equation because my life was lived spontaneously out of control.

Once Brian was out, I lived in the house alone for almost an entire extra month. He didn't need to know about it, and he still paid his portion of the monthly phone bill (which, even then, it was spotty and put a big rift in my trust in him). If he couldn't pay his half of the damned cell phone bill and would ghost for weeks at a time, how would I have trusted him to pay a mortgage that would be in my name? No matter how much he hated it, I was right on that accord. Even then, it was a battle to get my phone back. I still owed on it and couldn't afford it on my own anymore. My mom was due for an upgraded phone, luckily, and she cancelled her plan and hoped on over to mine so I could catch up on the bill and have someone I'd trust to pay on time.

I left the house vacant in the middle of August, 2017. There was a subtle ache inside the pit of my stomach that I could mask with the strenuousness moving of all my furniture with the help of my Aunt Mar, Uncle Chris, and sisters, Diana and Chelsey.

We did it all in one day and drank to a new, fresh, and light beginning at my new apartment in Dormont. It wasn't far from Dad's house, about four minutes to be exact, and it was close enough that I could keep an eye on the house while it still struggled to sell, but I didn't have to live in it or be in the middle of it every waking day. I was one step closer to mending what I'd carried with me for so long. It was scary, but it was beyond time to keep moving forward in an entirely new space with my new roommate, Samantha.

Chelsey came over a couple of times before the house sold and we talked about the fallout between Brian and me. I can't say I saw it coming, but our own fallout was not far behind. Dad owned a truck and a motorcycle, and my sister financially struggled with her husband, two adorable nieces, and awesome nephew, who was a little more like me than any of us expected. Because of their struggles, they had a hard time keeping a vehicle, and I wanted to help but also help myself. Kill two birds with one stone type of deal. I agreed to sell the truck to her way underpriced, but then she fell off the face of the planet for about three months.

"Hello? Are you ready to do the truck or what? I've been waiting," she finally text me on a Thursday after months of nothing but absence. Since then, she had unfriended me or deleted her Facebook account, and ignored messages from me. Now, granted, I only really sent one or two messages since she'd disappeared.

"Yeah," I kept it simple and direct.

"What was it again? $1,000-1,500?" she replied.

"$2,000, but I'll drop it to $1,500 to get it gone and be done with it."

"Okay," Chelsey hesitated. "I'll see what I can do. How does Sunday work?"

"Good to me," I sent over and pushed the encounter away until Sunday. It came. It passed. Chelsey never showed or messaged or called the day she said she would, which was alright, I suppose, because I wasn't sure how I felt about giving away the truck. For starters, it didn't start any longer. I didn't want my sister to buy something where she might have to put in a boatload of work into something when I knew they struggled already. On the other hand, it was Dad's truck and my sister wanted to hoard everything down to the floorboards of my Dad's stuff because his death struck her hard and relentlessly.

"Are we doing the truck or what?" she text me weeks after we were originally supposed to meet. As a stubborn Taurus, I ignored her message completely.

"Hello??" she responded thirty minutes later, while I played video games at my apartment because I was having a lazy, mental health Sunday (when I should have been writing, truthfully). Weeks passed while my friend Ryan, who I'd met at Trey's memorial, and I tried bringing the truck back to life. It needed a new battery, but that didn't make it start. I panicked and responded to my sister, hoping that the offer still stood.

"Hey."

"What's up?" Chelsey responded quicker than I expected.

"Still want the truck?" I waited, holding my breath for her reply—for relief from one less thing of Dad's.

"You waited too long. $1,000 or forget it," she spit fired.

"You can go fuck yourself with your money," I threw my phone after I sent the message and ignored the shit-storm that followed. "I don't need you," I whispered to myself in my apartment living room.

Those were the last times I talked to either of my siblings—siblings who stuck by me through a lot of my grief after Dad died. On the same hand, they brought a lot more mess
than there already was. I had no right to judge them for how they
grieved or acted in response to their grief. They filled some of
the biggest memories in Dad's house: When we played a game
we called "Small, Medium, or Large Guys" (basically, when we'd
play "small guys," it was small toys we had around and enact-
ed great battles that ended in a lot of imaginary explosions and
weird noises. "Medium guys" were the toys that were too big for
"small guys," and "big guys" were live reenactments of the same
toys just with our bodies). When my sister tried to make me eat
porridge that was rain water collected in a handrail hole in the
ground with mixed muddy leaves and bugs and a lot of other
gross things. She would splat it on rock plates and try to make
me eat it. I always pretended I did but spilled it out in the grass
when she wasn't looking. Where I learned to punch from my dad
and made the poor and regrettable choice of practicing on my
sister the day she got her first period (sorry, Chelsey). Where my
siblings would get spanked and sent to the corner for doing something all three of us did, but I'd be spared because they took a
lot of the brunt of punishment for me. No one liked the wooden
spoon Mom shook at us when we disobeyed.

Those memories flashed through my head in a heat wave
while I sat in a boardroom high up in a random office building in
downtown Pittsburgh. My boss sat next to me, who was buying
Dad's house for the medical practice for when patients were in
crisis, and she could help those who needed it.

"Vaughn and I were talking, and what if we walked away
and did this whole thing without a closing company to avoid all
these extra costs?" my boss folded her hands and leaned against

the table. My gaze dropped down to the envelope I had the administer papers for Dad's estate in, proving I had right to sell the home, plus a few checks in case I owed something at the end of it all.

"Are you kidding me?" the lawyer's face flashed bright red at my boss as I scratched into the envelope with my black pen in one line, back and forth until I could smell the ink. "What's the point of all of this then? This was a waste of time," he yelled and threw his pen.

"Look," my boss argued with him, "the closing of the house was supposed to help him. This brings us out at even and it's not helping him at all. I'm trying to work something out to help him. Do you understand what I'm saying?" She didn't break composure once.

"Call me back when you're ready to be serious about this," the lawyer got up from his seat like a little child, whining because he didn't get his way, and stomped off to his office.

"What do you want to do?" she asked me as my realtor sat dead quiet in her seat.

Jump out the window and end your life. It'll be a quick fall. That, or your heart is going to explode from inside with this stress.

I wanted my heart to explode so I didn't have to be there anymore. The meeting was hard enough, let alone the argument that just ensued between my boss, this lawyer, and my realtor, who went to school with my dad.

"I don't know what you want to do, Vaughn," my realtor spoke in the silence, "but I have to leave in about five minutes to go to another meeting in Wexford."

"What are you thinking?" my boss asked again.

"Let's just fucking do it and get it over with. I can't handle this stress, my anxiety is through the roof, and I need out of this hot office. I need to be done. I'm done," I set the pen down hard on the boardroom table and looked over at my boss, who smiled and leaned back in her chair.

"Can you get that little baby of a lawyer back in here, so we can settle up?" she pointed over at the door where the lawyer disappeared from, and my realtor uneasily shook her head and called for him. With the papers all lined across the table, I signed my dad's house away one paper at a time and closed the deal that I'd hoped would get me out of my financial crisis. At the end of it all, it only relieved me of my emotional burden from a house I let fall into disarray—my dad's pride and joy that he'd put so much blood, sweat, and tears into.

So much for keeping the house for the sake of your dad. He would be ashamed of you for how you let it fall to pieces, how you sold it away and didn't keep it until you met your end. You are weak. You are nothing. First your dad's house, then your family. You're a sad excuse for a son.

"It's fine that I didn't get any money," I whispered in the smoke-stained elevator with my boss only feet away from me.

"What?" she asked.

"My dad told me I'd always have that house, no matter what happened. I'd always have that house to come home to and live in if life got hard," I stuffed my hands into my pockets and shivered from the cold breeze pushing through the holes of the elevator doors.

"This is better for you and your anxiety," she texted on her phone as the elevator slowed to a stop and the double doors slid open to the main lobby.

Dad was wrong when he told me I'd always have the house. I left it so easily so many times, at least three when he was alive, and only stayed there to eat and sleep and pensively shower for way longer than I should let the water run. I wouldn't stay there, because it was never my house. I never felt I had ownership or a right to keep that house and call it my own. It was always Dad's house because, well, it was his house. There was nothing I could say, change, or do to make that house mine. There was no number of coats of paint I could slab on the walls to change that. His tie to his home reached beyond the walls I lived in for twenty-three years of my life. It was the end of the book for Dad's house on the hill, and I accepted the end. I welcomed it, the lift of burden and weight on my shoulders to be a twenty-three-year-old home-owner/landlord/mechanic/self-grief manager or whatever hat I'd end up wearing if I kept the house instead. It wasn't what the family wanted, but it was best for my personal health to block it out and let go. Beyond those walls, my dad will live in the memories of those who knew him and loved him; even the people who didn't deserve to know him or experience his selfless kindness.

More importantly, beyond those walls, after my boss changed everything inside that house so it could be made to help those who really need a home, I will live. I will live louder than the voices of my mental illness telling me how ashamed my dad would be of me or how I have failed. I have not failed. I will not live a life in captivity to my own self-degradation. I may not have Dad's house to come home to, but others will.

That is enough for me.

Chapter Twenty-Three
2018

A year ago, New Year's looked very different. I was with my family in Erie, Pennsylvania, swimming in the hotel pool, drinking, and pulling confetti poppers all over the hotel room. We ate food at local restaurants in modest downtown Erie, I dodged drunk and emotional siblings when I could, and managed when I couldn't. I watched my mom smile, genuinely, with her boyfriend as she watched her three kids together again for one of the last times she would see. Mom moved down to South Carolina with her boyfriend shortly after 2017 began. It was easier for her to breathe down in the warmer weather instead of up here in Pittsburgh's bitter cold. I missed her more than I could explain, and dropping her off at the airport the day she left was the closest I had come to crying in a long time. Mom cried hard. She felt awful for leaving me, but we both knew it was a necessity for her to heal with an entire section of her lung missing.

Amy Winehouse and Adele played in my best friend Amanda's vehicle while we traveled to Chicago to celebrate New Year's Eve with her friends, Kara and Ron. So much shit happened in a year. I went through four jobs, lost two people I loved dearly, created new friends, reconciled with ones I'd lost along the way, and got into a new relationship that was beautifully organic. My soul made up so much of my physical self that when it ached and cried out, I felt it all within my bones, muscles, and brain. Everything took a piece of me with it, all of the ups and downs and static in between, that I wasn't sure what was me or what was the ghost within the empathetic shell I called my body. It had been about a year since I visited Chicago last, and I missed it more than I realized. My soul missed it.

When I was there last, I went on a whim since I had an extra ticket credit with Amtrak and escaped Pittsburgh in February of 2017. I was losing control, forgetting who I was as I became washed out and a sickly beige color. I needed to hard reset my body and soul and restart, for even a moment in time, and so I escaped Pittsburgh for a long weekend and felt the city soundwaves align with mine in perfect harmony. Being there this time, at Fireside before the year ended, I remembered what I promised myself—something that became so easy to forget while I lost my job and was forced to start at ground zero—I will move to Chicago by the end of the year. It didn't happen, but the memory felt like I was seeing an old friend for the first time in years—like I saw my Dad and Trey again after their passing and had one last word with them. What would I say? What would I do? Probably stand there quietly, like I sat there at the head of the table.

I wasn't quiet because of discomfort or worry or anxiety. My mental illness failed to exist when I was in this city. That was never something I could explain to anyone, especially my boyfriend, Drew, who wanted so desperately to understand what went on inside this head of mine. Every time I'd start to explain the feeling, words just failed to describe and it all felt like childish injustice or epic disservice. While we drank and watched New York City ignite in colors and another dismal Mariah Carey performance (at least it was better than last year's), we fiddled on our phones or chatted lightly in conversation.

"Okay, so we have this tradition where each of us picks a word we want to describe our year to come. What would they be?" Someone in our friend group asked underneath the warm lights of the Fireside bar. Candles lit the tables and flickered each time the front door opened and ignited warm light on our faces as we spoke. Kara fiddled with her fingers as we all thought it over, mulled a million and one words we could think of that sounded sufficient enough to please our future desires and goals for the year.

"Productive," Kara looked up from the candlelight flickering inches away from her. The group of friends, most of whom I'd just met that day, nodded their heads and reinforced the power of speaking it out into the universe.

"Identity," Ron, Kara's boyfriend, followed her lead as we all spoke and explained why we chose the words we did.

"Absorbency," I spoke quietly as the clock counted down to the New Year. "There are a lot of new things coming up in this next year, a lot of important things that I want to be completely aware for. I want it to affect me and change me in the best way. I want to embrace whatever is going to come forward—good or bad, bright or dark. Whatever it is—," I bit my lip and worried if I'd spoken too much. I looked up and grabbed my empty beer bottle to avoid the social anxiety building in my stomach. The anxiety didn't have control over me, though. I didn't want to hide my face, run away into the frozen Chicago air, barricade myself in the bathroom, and the voices that I battled didn't cough out even one word. I was safe and in control of the scattered warmth from the constant opening and closing of the front door that gushed frigid winter air every time someone walked in or out.

"It's a great word," Amanda pulled her hand away from her mouth to speak and put it right back once she was done talking.

"Thanks. It took me a minute to figure it out. I'm so indecisive, but that one stuck most," I smiled and sipped the warm last gulp of my Miller Lite before setting it at the edge of the table.

"Yeah, I like that word a lot," Andrew reached down beneath the table and squeezed my leg, lovingly. He smiled and blinked blankly while I looked away from him and over at the bar area for another drink.

"Ball's going to drop soon!" he yelled as we all scatter-searched for the easiest television to watch. The ball began to drop in the one-minute countdown. The camera panned over the crowd as Andrew grabbed my hand. I held my breath as the clock counted down, second by second. Flash backs from the last year felt like I had swallowed dry ice, burned it down my throat and into my belly, where it fogged and boiled and burned. I looked over at Amanda as she rapidly texted her husband or Lindsey, Kara and Ron leaned into each other as his arm wrapped around her shoulders, while the others at the other end of the table counted out loud with the clock. The room wanted to spin, my vision wrapping it around and bogging it down within my brain as it translated. Part of me wanted to scream and try to stop the clock. The other part that was uncleanly split knew I needed this horrific year to end more than anything—not so I could leave it behind, but so I could move forward.

You're supposed to make New Year's resolutions: lose weight, find love, stop lying, and getting a new job were a few that came to mind. Survival was the only one that felt I could even hope for, let alone try and achieve. There was a lot to conquer for my survival of the next year, if it was going to be anything like the last. There had to be balance. *Oh God, I fucking hope there is balance in life.* It couldn't be as terrible as last year, or I didn't think I'd make it out alive. I didn't pray for nothing bad to ever happen to me because I learned the necessity for deep valleys to contrast high peaks. Otherwise, the lines of life would blur and I'd lose track of the truly great moments that defined our mortal timelines.

With fifteen seconds left, I felt my heartbeat pounding harder in my head as I continued to hold my breath. My grip on Andrew's hand felt cold and distant. I was all too aware of my existence in this last moment. Desperately, I grasped at the quick fleeting seconds in the hardest year I've had to date.

"Happy New Year!" The entire bar cheered as the television flashed brightly in the dim room. Andrew pulled our hands still wrapped together to the surface and rested them on the table.

"Happy New Year, babe," he leaned in to kiss me and I followed his lead as I let the end of the line rapidly disappear behind me.

"Happy New Year," our lips met like they had a million times before. He tasted like beer, but I did, too, with the lingering taste of light beer tingling on my tongue.

It was our second trip together, Andrew and I. We visited my mom down in South Caroline two weeks before we made the trip to Chicago for the New Year. We walked underneath millions of lights at a festival Mom wanted to take us to. He tried to teach me how to drive his manual transmission vehicle and it ended in a full-blown panic attack that I had to pull over and switch seats with him only thirty minutes into my turn to drive. We spent time on the beach together as my mom snuck photos of us looking out into the cloudy horizon before we disembarked for home. He was perfect. *We were perfect.*

He blew me away with how he played the bassoon and saxophone, striking a gig down in West Virginia for the yearly Italian Festival. We traveled down to practice a few times, stopping at his brother and sister-in-law's home in the absolutely beautiful middle-of-nowhere, West Virginia. That visit gifted him a trip to three hospitals when a copperhead lunged for his ankle from underneath one of the vehicles. I stayed by his side, sleeping in the guest chair at Ruby Memorial Hospital in Morgantown. By far, probably one of the longest weekends I'd had in a while, but with him there, I didn't mind spending my weekend in a hospital. He made it bearable, even if his ankle was blown up to the size of a small balloon. If we could make it through an entire weekend in the hospital, undamaged other than his ankle, we could conquer the world together.

I believed we could, until the Chicago trip ended. As we left the city in Amanda's car in, yet again, another snowstorm in Indiana, my mood shifted. Everything became covered in shade and darkness. I was in this car, trapped, and suffocating. He watched television as Amanda and I chatted about podcasts, books, and all things writing. We fleshed out some verbal planning for the memoir that you're reading right now as I tumbled downward into the arms of the voices that slowly crept back in the farther we got from Chicago. I didn't want to leave. No part of me wanted to head back to Pittsburgh or make it out of that snowstorm. I wanted to turn back around and head to the city where the voices were silenced and I flourished. I hadn't realized how much I still lived with this illness and how much it clouded over my body, mind, and soul until I was plucked out of it and let to breathe in fresh air for the first time.

Don't misunderstand me. Andrew made me so incredibly happy. He was a kind soul, loving, and all-encompassing, a phenomenal human. Life was truly beautiful with him in it and I was comfortable in our habits and adventures. It wasn't Andrew I was tired of. It was Pittsburgh that I needed to escape from. While I poured out my story to my best friend, Amanda, Andrew slept in the backseat and didn't squeak a single sound. He didn't want to be in that car. Not because of the car itself, but we had just come back from a long drive down to my mom's two weeks before. We were worn out from long car rides. To save myself from the panic rising as we crossed into Ohio, I talked about things I'd never admitted to even Andrew. Truth be told, I forgot he was there for a moment as I spiraled down into the memories I kept locked away in the drawer within my mind, left open to pour out and overflow when I unlocked them. I spoke above the fast-paced palpitations beating inside my heart until there was nothing left other than scabs of all the things that plagued me—haunting me into each passing year.

"Write your story," Amanda pushed further. "You just need to stop doubting yourself and do it. You'll feel a million times better, I promise you."

"You think?" I asked, seeing the gleaming light at the end of my agonizing tunnel within the bright exit ramp lights.

"Totally," she scratched her nose and sipped coffee while we drove into the night toward home.

I ended it with Andrew shortly after we got back from the trip, but not before torturing him for a month when I fell into my yearly seasonal depressive spell. This year was worse—like an addict coming down from the biggest high. I secluded myself from the world, from Andrew, as I soul-searched alone. It was the only way I could truly figure out what was wrong with me. I cut deep into him, into his feelings, as I ignored him for days on end while the depressive and anxious voices chattered away inside my head about how terrible of a human I was to hurt someone I loved so much.

Do I love him? Do people that are in love with someone treat them like this? Maybe it was just me and my sickness—cursed with the loss and grief I'd endured in the past year. Maybe, after all that time of trying to convince myself I wasn't, I was damaged goods. Outdated, expired, and coming to the ultimate end. I wondered what it would feel like to end it here. I thought about the pain I'd cause once I was gone. I read over Trey's memorial flyer, my father's obituary that I wrote, watched movie after movie, and cried alone. Come see the broken man, driven by emotional self-harm to continually suffer. Come see this never-before-seen circus act as he, single handedly, destroys everything good in his world. Step right up to the *freak show.*

January and February were my hardest months of survival. Incredible self-care followed and a lot less emotional self-deprecation. Amanda took me under her wing once I admitted where my headspaces took me, and some that I kept secret from even her, and she showed me how to heal myself through the brokenness. You had to use your own weapon against itself—turning the worst parts into a gleaming sword to cut through and conquer the darkness I reveled in after so many nights. "Good-selfish" was my secondary word for 2018 as I leveled out and the weather cleared. I survived those hard months, clearer than I was when I entered into that year, but Andrew and I didn't survive the war.

"Most of my breakups happened in January and February," I admitted to him late one night over text.

"You couldn't have told me that earlier?" he laughed about it, but I could feel the hurt in his joke. He wasn't really joking.

"Yeah, I guess I should have. I'm sorry," I admitted and pulled the covers up to my eyes.

"I'm glad you're feeling better now, though. I am, too. I've been focusing on school, moving, laying low at work to move further up the corporate America totem pole. I've been doing much better," he replied as sleep drug down my eyelids.

"I love you," I sent as my eyelids dropped heavy. I loved him. I still do and I'm positive I always will—whether we end up together in the future or not, while I go explore the rest of my life, change it one step at a time and make moves toward moving to Chicago, it doesn't matter. I'll have him tucked away in my heart and will try to love myself as much as he endlessly and unashamedly loved me. We may not have survived 2018 together, but we would undoubtedly survive a lifetime together.

Chapter Twenty-Four
QUEENDOM

Andrew and I ended shortly after we came home from Chicago. I felt stuck in this dark glass prism where I was being bent and split into a million different parts and colors. I was thinned out into a watered-down existence, translucent and floating like sea dust in the darkest, deepest part of an endless ocean. My heart screamed but my lips pursed closed tighter. Blood dripped into my mouth from where my teeth sunk into chapped lips and raw skin. My body was lumpy and misshapen. Fat and full of sorrow, stress eating until I got tired and frustrated with how stagnant and complacent I'd allowed myself to become.

The Fates are not old or decrepit like in the stories. History had it wrong. For me, at least. The Fates, my Fates, were three strong, beautiful women that created the three corners of my prism. They were not the ones who created the struggle or kept the lingering pain thriving. The entire time, through the crying, endless struggle, rogue sorrow, and scattered light in the glass I scratched as I resisted the refraction, they waited patiently in the three corners. These women watched and warned as I created the cloud around my head and became lost in my own grief. I created the struggle when the glass was clearer than crystal. They provided the end of the prism where I could pass through and become changed. I brought my mess with me and it scattered all light. I lost myself in my grief and mental illness, forgot my identity, and the other end of the prism where I was supposed to come out of disappeared from my line of sight.

My less-ominous Fates had names, and instead of existential thread, they spooled out their insight. Together, Amanda, Jordan, and Diana beautifully spun the thread of possibility and hope with her hands, allotted the thread with their courage, and brought the inevitable end to the surface. They showed me the end of my darkness, the possibility of a different life as they guided me through the untangling of the mess I'd created inside my prism. Even though they all didn't appear in my life at the same time, like some storm of destiny and indisputable fate, I clearly remember the day I realized who they were to me.

Toledo, Ohio. 2018.

We sat high up in The Heights, a cement and glass room at the top of the Renaissance Hotel, warmly lit with murphy bulbs. Amanda, Diana, Jordan, and I celebrated after an incredible writing event they'd hosted in a refurbished dining complex along the river. Three of us ordered prosecco, a tradition for Amanda and Jordan that I followed in line with because the menu triggered mild social anxiety for me, and Diana ordered a glass of wine. Dark grey painted cement covered the floor and met the corner of the room where glass walls showed the dark and electric city sky. I felt far away from these three incredible women I wanted to be the most like, even with them sitting so close to me. As they talked about future plans, their goals intertwining with each other, I sat there in quiet admiration, stifled by all of the strength in one room.

You will never be one of them.

Why not? I have a story…

You can't even publish the book you already wrote. What makes you think you have any ground here, any chance to even achieve a sliver of what they have created?

I have them, though. That's something. They believe in me.

That makes three people. You don't even believe in yourself.

No, I don't. Maybe you're right. Maybe I'll always be on the other side of this wall, always too far, yet so close I could almost reach out and feel the strength and light and change. I didn't want to always feel like I was on the other side of this wall, though. I wanted to be with them, experiencing the triumphs with them, and cheering them on like they do for me.

Forget it. You won't make it. You'll always be an almost. Almost reaching your goals. Almost over the grief, but never fully healed. You're not one of them. They are much more than who you will ever become. This is their domain. There is no space for you.

I gulped down a mouthful of bitter, bubbly prosecco and felt it burn down my throat. It was dark enough to hide the tears welling in my eyes in front of them. They didn't notice, but I was an expert at hiding my sadness by now. I perfected my fake laughter to express correctly on queue with the expressions of the others, so I could drown in the darkness whispering self-proclaimed faults and failures in my ear.

"So, Mr. Vaughn, Vaughn-Shane! What're you doing? What's going on in your life?" Diana asked after she sipped her red wine, crossed her legs, and leaned in to listen to me, like every word I was about to say were the most important words she'd ever hear.

"Me?" I asked to clear the frog nesting in my throat. "Well," I spoke in a faded laugh as the music picked up and my buzz vibrated with the flashing red lights across the river. "I'm exploring this memoir of mine right now. Kind of hit a hard point and a big block, went into a deep, deep depression and stopped. I'm trying. It's hard. I, uh—had to go through a really dark patch a couple weeks ago. I tried to self-medicate my mental illness, tried to properly medicate my mental illness when that didn't succeed and, even then, it didn't really work for me. Tonight was necessary. This trip away from Pittsburgh is everything to me. Being around you three is incredible. It's hard to explain, but I really, really appreciate it and love it a lot."

"You just need to sit down and write it," Amanda smiled directly across from where I sat. "The story's in there. Just do it and write it!" she laughed and sipped her prosecco. Jordan nodded and sat comfortably cross-legged in her seat, the lights shining brilliantly against her glasses.

You can't do it. It's not that easy. You're not ready to dive deep and unbury me, where it's comfortable and warm underneath.

Maybe you're right. But it's not warm like the sun where you hide inside my head. Surrounding me with all of my grief and pain wasn't comfortable, either. It was draining and soul-crushing and relentless. The waves weren't clear water, but an entire ocean littered with debris that stabbed at my feet when the water hit them. You dragged me into the undertow and sent me off to sea to drown. It was a suicide mission because the *"you"* I talked about was only ever *me*. I did this. *Me*. I saw their paradise, the Queendom, when the water sucked into my lungs for the last time and drowned me as I sat there at The Heights. Before I drifted down to the bottom of the black ocean floor, dirty water filling in the spaces inside my lungs as it hardened into black smoke-filled glass, I opened my eyes and let their words sink into me.

You let yourself drown every time. There was no evil force bringing you down and dragging you to drown in the nothingness. This was you. They can give you strength and inspiration and courage, that wasn't the problem. You had to save yourself. No one else had the power to drag you up to the surface. Before I sunk deep into the quicksand at the bottom of my black ocean, I kicked off the bottom and floated to the surface. I let the water drown my doubt and found the light when I reached the top. I swam hard back to reality, toward the Queendom that would anchor me when I heard my voice calling me back into the ocean to drown.

I wouldn't say that this was goodbye to my mental illness. It was a turning point. The beginning of untangling the prism I darkened where these three women, whether they knew it or not, guided me through the hardest parts. At the very least, I owed them my thanks for showing and reminding me of the scintillate light that was inside of me all this time. I just needed to open my eyes, grab a hold of it, and kick off the ground on my own. No one else could have done that for me.

Chapter Twenty-Five
WHAT WOULDN'T I GIVE

I've asked myself this question a lot in the past six years. What wouldn't I give to go back and undo the amount of crazy debt I accrued, if I would've chosen differently the ones who I gave my body to, and who I'd keep in better contact with and who I'd easily let slip away into a different lifetime—a lifetime where our paths never crossed. All of those little things feel minor in the grand scheme of it all. Maybe that's why we don't have superpowers? There are no spells or time machines to take us back to redo the past, simply a million and one directions we can choose to take in our present.

Oddly, I think about the end of my time a lot. Not that I'm looking forward to it or wanting it to happen any time soon, no, but what it might look like. Maybe I think about it a little too much, actually, from my anxiety. Sometimes it's nice to be reminded that you only get one shot at it. It's helped me edge out a lot of anger I held, a lot of pain, and a lot of half-life love. Not knowing the end is kinder for us. Unlike some, we aren't allotted to know when the end of our line will be or what it will look like. We are given the here and now and the chances to make change, leave our marks, and pass kindness onto others. We live on in the memories of the ones we touch in our lives, not by our anxieties, our arguments, or our things.

I was driving through the sleepy suburbs of Baldwin, on my way home from watching movies over my best friend's house, when I remembered a night, years ago, when I was the most defeated in my craft—when I doubted my writing, wrote hate to myself on little pieces of paper about how I will never amount to any kind of writer; that, with my luck, I would surely die before I published any kind of book. Mind you, this was way before I lost my dad and Trey. This was a time when I was just over eighteen, figuring out life, getting drunk, and giving out my love like a cheap gas station keychain to anyone who would carry it with them.

"I would give anything—*anything*—in the world to be published," I said to myself in the dark of my bedroom on the steepest street in the world. Dad and Char were asleep in the bedroom next to me with the Investigation Discovery channel mumbling in low volume under Dad's snoring. I cried myself to sleep that night. It might sound silly, honestly, but it was the rawest ache inside the pit of my stomach—the ache of an artist who wanted to share their gift with the world. Sharing it was how I felt important. It was how I'd leave my mark on this world, how I'd stop worrying about failing college and having small jobs that never really amounted to anything. It was going to be my big break in life. Strangers would start to care about what I was saying and maybe love wouldn't hurt as much when you're a young gay kid who only felt important when he was giving his body to someone. *What wouldn't I give to be published?*

As I drove home, listening to moody electronic music, it hit me like I'd hit a deer in the middle of the road. *Prismatic* wouldn't have existed without the loss of my dad. Yeah, I've been through a lot before then, but really, what would it be without my loss? Then Trey? Would I know some of the amazing people I've come to meet and become close to without losing two people I loved? Would you be reading this right now?

I can't tell you how many times I've asked myself, if I was given the option, would I go back and save them at the cost of my craft?

Of course.

If my dad never passed away, though, I would have never met Trey. I'd still be living at Dad's house, playing video games, or reading, or eating dinner with him, leaning next to the stove as the evening light cast his body in silhouette. Char would be outside smoking a cigarette, nodding off in our hidden oasis in the house on the hill. My siblings and I would probably still be on good terms with each other. I might still be working at the hotel. Mom might still be here in Pennsylvania, but I think she would've ended up in South Carolina regardless (she's always been a beach bird). Would I have ever been as close with Amanda, or come to know Diana and Jordan? What would things with Andrew and my life look like? Would we even have met?

Loss changes lives whether we want it to or not. It is how we connect with other, how we feel empathy when we might not want to or have the ability to. Whether it is loss of a loved one, loss of a relationship, loss of a job, loss of money, or loss of everything you've ever come to know or be familiar with, we all *feel it*. Loss does more than just strip you down to bare bones and guttural emotion. It gives you the opportunity to become grounded again, to remember what's really important in your life and what you really care about. It reminds us that we are humans no matter what we identify as, what the tone of our skin is, who we love, or what our beliefs are.

Although very unlikely, I hope you never feel what it's like to truly lose something or someone you love. I don't wish that pain on anyone, no matter if you're my enemy, or if you don't believe in any of my beliefs. What you can't discredit is that, on the most basic level of understanding, we are human. We lie, we cheat, we say things that we regret, and we fuck up. But through all the mess we surround ourselves in or fall into, we are human.

I think a lot less about *what I wouldn't give to change my life* and more about *what I can do to change the lives of others.* We can't change the past and we can't predict the future, so what are we going to do?

We make change.

ACKNOWLEDGEMENTS

MOM. Thank you for always being my tether to faith. Even though our visions of what that looks like may differ, you always believed in me and reminded me that God had a plan and it was this. I love you so, so much.

DAD. I wish you could read this book. You'll always be the image of strength and resiliency for me, and your "buddy boy" will endlessly look up to you. Thank you for your selflessness and sacrifice throughout my twenty-two years of living that you got to be there for and keep watching out for me as I keep on keeping on. I love you.

CHELSEY. Sister, I'm so thankful to call myself your little brother. Even if we don't talk much now, you were an incredible role model for me and you always accepted me as who I was, even before I even knew who I was. Even though this book was a lot of our darkest moments together as a family, I hope you know that I will always love you regardless of how our lifetimes align again in the future. You will always be my incredibly gracious, loving, and loyal sister, no matter what.

BRIAN. You are the best big brother I could've ever asked for. Thanks for being there for so much after Dad died and thank you for taking the reins and doing the difficult things when I didn't want to or shied away from those difficulties. Also, thanks for putting up with my bullshit when I was being THE MOST extra. I appreciate you more than you might know. ***gives you and Chels all the energies***

DIANA, CHANNING, & EXTENDED FAMILY. Thank you so much for coming into my life and really believing in me and being gracious and kind. I'm so glad to have met you guys and that you could be a part of this journey with me. You all mean the absolute most to me.

THE SIBS. Your chapter basically sums this up, but I don't know what I would do without all of you by my side the entire way. You've watched me grow up, helped me through the hardest moments and kept me afloat. Thank you a million times over and I hope you know this book is not only a dedication to Dad, but also the biggest thank you for all the support you've effortlessly given.

AMANDA. Honestly, what am I supposed to even say? First, I love you. Legit. Without your fierce support, hard work, incredible talent, heart, and kindness (I could physically go on forever), I would not be where I am today. This book would not have happened. It doesn't even come close to how I feel but THANK YOU. I can't wait to see what we accomplish next and I will always be on your team, no matter what! Let's do some crazy creative shit and take over the world, yeah? Sweet.

RYAN. Thank you for lending your nifty gifties, time, and support, and I'm so grateful I can call you friend.

DIANA. I've told you this so many times before, but thank you for being so damn inspirational, kind, and a huge emotional driver for me to keep pushing forward no matter what. Knowing you and your story played a huge part in writing all of the hard parts of mine, and there are no words that come close to thanking you for sharing your faith. I thank God for bringing such an incredible person into my life.

JORDAN. Girl. You helped me start this whole thing back at the first Write to Heal event. I thought you were the coolest person, hysterical, and that you looked like Jennifer Lawrence (all things still true). Jokes aside, I'm awestruck in the amount of strength you show every single day and I'm so incredibly thankful I can call you friend and a huge part of my Queendom. I appreciate you forever and a day, and I can't wait to see how you change the world next!

MS. FOX. Thank you for never giving up on the little troubled kid who hated English all those years ago. You supported me, gave me insight, and brought me into my world of words, and there is nothing on this planet that could show how thankful I am for you. The world needs more teachers like you.

READERS. Thank you for believing in this book, whether I know you personally or not. This journey was one of the most challenging I've had to overcome, and that's saying a lot considering all of the things I've lived through so far. But, here we are, so thank you.

CPSIA information can be obtained
at www.ICGtesting.com
Printed in the USA
BVHW08s1303050918
526587BV00009B/364/P